AIDS PANDEMIC
The Untold Story

Dorothy writes her book at a critical time. COVID-19 and AIDS are different viruses – but pandemics lay bare the inequities and problems in our social order and the programs we create to solve problems.

—*Tom Sheridan, Author of* Helping the Good Do Better

I predict this book will be a cornerstone in the histories of HIV/AIDS that will be written in the future.

—*Thad Zajdowicz, MD, MPH*

This thoughtfully crafted book reminds us all that with steely determination one person can change the world. It's hope in a paperback.

—*Jeanne Blake, Leadership Advisor and Journalist*

This book is so thoughtfully laid out. The connection to the current pandemic is perfect. Although some of the reminiscences of the dark days are difficult to wade through, the timeliness and importance of your message is really outstanding.

—*Susan Kendall Newman, Social Activist/Philanthropist*

This is a book that is revealing, in some cases shocking, in others heartbreaking and heartwarming. As a collection of diverse anecdotes, stories and memories whose tales are as individual as the authors sharing them, the overall effect is not one of a spectacular success story. Rather, it is a collection of small gems that tells us about the humanity and commitment of these advocates.

—*William Arnold, ADAP Working Group Co-Founder;*
Founding Director/CEO of the Community Access National Network

It should be assigned reading for young people looking for how to live out their ideals, but also to those with an interest in American social history.

—*Arthur Adelberg*

AIDS PANDEMIC
The Untold Story

A Guide to Making a Difference

Dorothy Keville
with Barbara Hesselgrave

AIDS Pandemic - The Untold Story
by Dorothy A Keville
with Barbara Hesselgrave

HIV/AIDS; Public Policy; Healthcare; Activists; Stigma

Cover Art by Thad Zajdowicz, MD, MPH
Author Photo by Clara Miller

Cover/interior design for 1st edition by Jim R. Garrison
Additional cover/interior design for 2nd edition by Ryan Forsythe

Print ISBN-13: 978-0-578-30258-4
Ebook ISBN-13: 978-0-578-30323-9

Published by Pathtowrite Press • October 2021

DEDICATION

Thank you to my biggest support group, my children
Kathy, Karen, Patti, Tom and Bill

This book is dedicated to the memory of John Francis Folby, former Pennsylvania State AIDS Director from 1987 to 2011. He credited the advocacy group ACT UP (AIDS Coalition to Unleash Power) for their aggressive efforts against this disease. He reminded us that at the beginning of his tenure, there was only AZT to treat the disease and when he left government service there were more than 700 drugs for treatment.

"Our responsibility is historic. When the history of AIDS and the global response is written, our most precious contribution may well be that, during a time of plague, we did not flee, we did not hide, and we did not separate ourselves from its risk. Hope for the tens of millions still afflicted by HIV currently still depends on scientists, practitioners, and citizens working together."

Jonathan Mann, MD
Geneva 50th Anniversary of the
Universal Declaration of Human Rights, 2011

RYAN WHITE COMPREHENSIVE AIDS RESOURCES EMERGENCY ACT OF 1990

CONTENTS

FOREWORD

This book is of importance in introducing readers to Dorothy Keville and her work that was the cornerstone effort in facilitating the first Federally funded program for HIV/AIDS drugs. When she began more than three decades ago, hers was a revolutionary concept, and in the mid-1990's there was a new and unknown disease named HIV/AIDS that needed a revolution in attitude, approach and funding.

With her generous manner and savvy insight to human behavior she masterminded unheard of collaboration bringing together angry activists, conservative politicians and unwilling drug manufacturers to Get Things Done.

That work ultimately evolved into a team called the AIDS Drug Assistance Program (ADAP) Working Group, and I was a key member as well. This initiative provided medicine and care for HIV positive people in all U.S. States and Territories. Critically important however, this book also introduces us to the ADAP managers and directors, part of that cadre of so many unsung heroes whose contributions to the HIV/AIDS community, truly legendary in scope, has up until now gone unrecognized.

Working in under-resourced offices, these state government individuals who were hired to manage this new program labored tirelessly for years, decades, and for some their entire career life to overcome incredible obstacles in caring for people with HIV/AIDS. In the stories shared within this book they report they had no idea what they were getting themselves into. And it was a round-the-clock job that often broke their spirits, their relationships, and their hearts. But to a one they say it was the best thing they could have ever done. Through them, Dorothy brings us into their day-to-day challenges, showing us a behind the scenes illustration of incredible dedication to secure a better life for people with HIV/AIDS.

No one knows these stories of how in that era there was no office manual to follow, no standard operating procedures, no client/agency guidelines. Literally, there was nothing but file folders in desk drawers, a telephone, and individual initiative. As word got out about the program then the phone rang off the hook and those files were jammed with the names of clients desperate to get medicine. As so many of them share here, you just did what you had to do, and that often included bending the rules. We all got plenty of practice doing that.

One of the most compelling features of these recollections is how HIV/AIDS was different from any other national health crisis. It came from nowhere and people affected were subjected to severe and punitive measures across every level of our society. This was unheard of.

As one of the original activists I can state unequivocally it was essential to learn how to face all these new circumstances, medically, politically, and socially. But no one knew what to do and everyone involved had to develop new skills, tactics and methods in a highly stigmatized and anti-AIDS political atmosphere.

One leading factor that we as activists all agreed upon was there could be no more "business as usual" by drug companies, lobbyists, Members of Congress and their staffs; all the way up to the White House. Moreover, it was essential for us to work together, as only unity could move Congress to act.

I look back now and see that we all had crucially necessary skills, knowledge and contacts at key moments over the years. But it was largely through the perseverance of Dorothy Keville that we were able to reduce the fractious attitudes and continue to move forward, and not fall apart in focusing on our individual agendas.

Today, when we naturally expect AIDS political support and program funding, it is hard to imagine how in that earlier era it was a crisis of begging and pleading for money to keep people alive. The breakthrough success came from the passing of the Federally funded Ryan White CARE Act. But when the first effective HIV treatment was developed its price tag of nearly $10,000 a year was crippling, putting it out of reach for most.

This then, was the pivotal moment when Dorothy joined the fight for equitable treatment. It was her finesse in negotiation and skill in listening that she fostered collaborations and advanced the concept of working together. As she put it, focus on the Big Picture. We needed to get substantial money to bring widespread access to HIV medicine and she was very adamant in saying that handcuffing yourself to a desk wasn't helping our cause. Like the demanding mom she was, she got everyone to behave. And we did get initial money, not all of it, but it was a good start.

Without her it is possible the ADAP Working Group effort may have failed in raising essential Federal funding. Thankfully, the "mom of ADAP" succeeded, and 25 plus years later, our Federal funding is solid and measured annually at $900.3M.

Even so, funding was just the first step. Making sure people actually got the medicine was due to the heroic efforts of the creativity and ingenuity of the administrators down in the trenches. They were the ones who put the money, the program and the people into action to make it all work. In this book she has successfully offered us a real-life snapshot of some of them, who in their own words describe how they faced challenges, forged new pathways and faced the ever-uphill battles on a daily basis.

They speak to the lack of data and how through their power of commitment and persuasion, racing against the AIDS death counts, they were able to gain access for as many HIV + as possible. HIV/AIDS was more than taking medicine: administrators collected data, helped people with housing, mental health, homelessness, drug addiction and the overwhelming despair and alienation so common among people with AIDS.

And then, we finally began to see there was a new understanding, and a new acceptance by communities, families, churches and institutions. Now, our new focus was how do we broadcast awareness on prevention and contain the spread of disease and help people try to live a normal life without fear of losing their job, their insurance and their families.

It is a different world today, and there are many younger generations who will be appalled to learn that you had to hide your status and your disease condition for fear of losing your lease, being denied a car loan, or being told to wash your clothes separately and eat off paper plates.

These lessons of the past and how they were overcome will be a painful eye opener to many and I hope that for readers learning this story for the first time there will be a new appreciation for how far we have come.

But this book only brings us a handful of the stories and they are the tip of the iceberg. There are tens of thousands of unsung heroes scattered throughout the AIDS advocacy world; I knew hundreds of them by name. Sadly, many are no longer with us and many are now elderly and infirm and unable to share their memories.

The legacy of their contribution however is not forgotten. While it's not too late, it soon will be, to acknowledge those critical efforts whether from the drug industry world, the AIDS advocacy world, or from Federal or state government. Their stories should be acknowledged and preserved. It would be my hope that people who are HIV+ today will appreciate this crucial history as many of them would not be here without the work of their preceding generations.

Dorothy shares in Part Two how she made it her mission to help people who had no voice of their own. From volunteer work with her children's schools, to local town councils, state governments and then positions with Federal agencies and multinational corporations, you will learn of her work in public policy for HIV, the homeless, breast cancer and becoming an actor.

This is a book that is revealing, in some cases shocking, in others heartbreaking and heartwarming. As a collection of diverse anecdotes, stories and memories whose tales are as individual as the authors sharing them, the overall effect is not one of a spectacular success story. Rather, it is a collection of small gems that tells us about the humanity and commitment of these advocates.

William Arnold is the Founding Director, President, and CEO of the Community Access National Network, and Co-founder of the ADAP Working Group

AIDS PANDEMIC
The Untold Story

A Guide to Making a Difference

INTRODUCTION

This book came about after I invited the former 50 state AIDS Directors to share their stories of the early days of the HIV/AIDS pandemic. Many are no longer with us and some were unable to be found, but those who are still here have given me their stories located in Part One. In doing a historical perspective of these early AIDS memoirs, representing all parts of the nation, we learn how in-the trenches efforts were able to get that pandemic under control.

I have many hopes for my readers in doing this collection. One is that you will gain a unique insight to how very differently the world looked at the disease decades ago; the challenges that faced the medical, scientific and government arenas and moreover, the incredible obstacles the people with this virus had to live through.

This book may also help encourage those who might not know their HIV status to get tested. I also hope that my story, which is in Part Two may spark an interest in students, or anyone really, to learn more about public policy and how each person with a passion can work for the greater good of all.

Each recollection that follows is unique. In the end, I hope that you find inspiration and learn about this amazing little known history. Finally, it would be my wish that everyone might be motivated by these stories of compassion and dedication so that in some way, large or small, they help to enrich your own life.

Dorothy Keville, M.Ed
Founder and former Co-chair AIDS Drug Assistance Program
(ADAP) Working Group

PART ONE

It's the spring of 2020, alone and isolated in my 14th floor apartment overlooking Tampa Bay, I am in what's called lockdown, that new term that has become an everyday language from the COVID-19 crisis. Ordered by the Federal and state government, it's a little bit like martial law but mandated by health officials.

Facing the prospect of being cloistered in these four walls for perhaps weeks or months, I am remembering the success of my work during the HIV/AIDS crisis many years ago. I believe the nation's experience with COVID-19 compares to how it experienced HIV/AIDS. I decided to write about how my colleagues and I worked to solve a key aspect of the successful treatment of People With AIDS (PWAs).

As I anticipate taking on this project while the news bulletins report increasingly alarming information, I am even more convinced of the stunning parallels between these two viruses.

Both then and now scientific researchers have to contend with contact spread while searching for drug treatments and a vaccine.

Getting infected with HIV/AIDS was a confirmed death sentence. People living with AIDS lost the ability to fight off common colds, Kaposi's sarcoma, AIDS-related pneumonia and cancer. Scientists eventually discovered that the source of this disease was a Human Immunodeficiency Virus (HIV).

A recollection from one of my early national public health jobs stands out. It started with an appointment in 1980 as a Fellow working with

Patricia Harris, Secretary of the U.S. Department of Health and Human Services (HHS) in Washington, D.C. In retrospect, I didn't so much as choose a career path, it was more like I walked through an open door and it chose me. In the early '80s, HIV/AIDS was a virus that seemed to appear out of nowhere. It was different from anything else: Other viral invasions are repulsed and "cleared" by the body's immune system. But not AIDS.

My reminiscence is suddenly interrupted by a cable news alert. Alarming statistics detail the increasing spread of COVID-19 throughout the world. Our government's early response to AIDS then, and to COVID-19 now, was characterized by the same uncertainty and misinformation.

I recalled how 40 years ago, I was in my office just steps away from the HHS Secretary when we started receiving reports of gravely ill men in the New York and San Francisco area. The experts thought at first that they had a rare form of pneumonia caused by a weakened immune system, and people affected in the communities where the new virus surfaced were in a panic. This was the spring of 1981.

The Centers for Disease Control (CDC) created a task force to identify the source of this new virus. By the end of the year, the task force found a common thread in an unexpected population: gay men. It was named "Acquired Immunodeficiency Syndrome," which was shortened to AIDS. However, it wasn't long before it was known as the pejorative "gay plague."

Then, in 1982, infants and adults receiving blood transfusions were also getting ill with the same symptoms as gay men. Investigators found that this strange disease was being transmitted by both infected blood and sexual contact. They didn't know it at first, but they were battling a lethal retrovirus that quickly disabled the immune system.

In the present coping with the emergence of COVID-19 and how it impacts all facets of society, we need to look at experts with perspective. I can think of no one better to guide us in COVID-19 than Paul Volberding, MD.

EXPERT INSIGHTS - PAST EXPERIENCE TO COPE WITH THE PRESENT

Paul Volberding, MD

Paul founded the first inpatient ward for persons with AIDS in the San Francisco General Hospital and is today the Co-Director of the Center for AIDS Research at the University of California, San Francisco. Here is his very sage observation and insight on what we face today framed in the context from what we have learned in the past.

Our response to the early AIDS epidemic taught us many lessons, some of which are quite relevant to our facing the coronavirus pandemic. But the situation today has unique features as well, and we are clearly learning as we move. In the AIDS epidemic, we at first knew nothing of the causative agent, HIV, and had no way to diagnose infection. Quite early, though, we had the sense that not everyone was at the same level of risk.

As we saw most cases in gay men and injection drug users, we began to guess that AIDS was somehow associated with sexual activity and was also blood borne. Healthcare workers seemed generally spared although for some time we did have personal concerns. -I certainly did.

Over time, we realized that HIV was being spread from asymptomatic persons over a period of years in many cases. Once symptoms appeared, the mortality was essentially 100% until 15 years into the epidemic when, in 1996, we first had access to effective therapy. SARS-CoV-2 and its disease, COVID-19, is also spread from asymptomatic infection, but probably only for a short time, days to probably less than one to two weeks. The mortality from infection varies depending on factors we are still learning but is probably only 1% in large population surveys.

The problem with COVID-19, of course, is that it spreads very easily by respiratory routes and everyone is at equal risk. And healthcare workers at the front lines have perhaps the highest risk of infection. Still, fear of COVID-19 is very real, worldwide.

Lessons learned from AIDS that should be remembered now including the need to rely on factual evidence and public health measures and the importance of leaders who understand the issues and convey empathy without false optimism or manipulating fear. While we still have no HIV vaccine, we must sincerely hope that we can do better, and quickly, in our current crisis.

REAL ADVOCACY, REAL STORIES OF HISTORIC CHANGE

Tom Sheridan, The Sheridan Group

Tom Sheridan caught my attention in the late 1980's while he was with the Child Welfare League of America. Since then, I have followed his career of helping disadvantaged groups. His book, **Helping the Good Do Better** is an insightful collection of real life advocacy stories.

From my perspective I am very enthusiastic about the work of Dorothy Keville who inarguably writes her book at a critical time. In 2019 when I wrote my book, Helping the Good Do Better my intent was to focus on showcasing that even in critical and uncertain times, there is always opportunity for change. To illustrate, I opened with a chapter on AIDS and the Ryan White CARE Act as it truly demonstrates perfectly how collaboration can work to get things done. This was an amazing journey and I am so proud to have been a key proponent in bringing together individuals who otherwise might never have done this alone.

On April 24, 1990 a young hemophiliac named Ryan White, who seven years earlier had been diagnosed with HIV that had been acquired from a blood transfusion, died at the age of 18. His mother Jeanne helped gather AIDS advocates together with an idea that his story should be told at the highest levels. I was able to bring together Jeanne and her group of activists, with the actor Elizabeth Taylor who was notable in helping AIDS issues gain attention. Together we told Ryan White's story to Congress and expressed the important need for a national policy addressing HIV/AIDS issues. This cohesive effort worked, and we helped to pass the bill that was then named the Ryan White CARE Act, in honor of her son.

This was benchmark legislation that had many healthcare key elements for HIV/AIDS people. One of those was critically important in that it would later pave the way for people who had little or no insurance to be able to pay for crucially needed medicines. That program, now known as the AIDS Drug Assistance Program (ADAP) was advanced by Dorothy's commitment.

Decades later little did we know that another pandemic was about to test our strength as people, nations and citizens of the world. While COVID-19 and AIDS are different viruses, pandemics lay bare the inequities and problems both in our social order and in how we create the programs to solve them. This is a clear signal we need to change the course of effort and presents as well, the case of urgent need for all of us to care for each other as citizens.

SURVIVAL FROM BEHIND BARS

Pamela Smart, July 30, 2020

My niece Pame has been incarcerated in the Bedford Hills Correctional Facility in New York since the age of 23. She was convicted of conspiracy to commit murder, witness tampering and accomplice to first degree murder, receiving a sentence of life without parole. She maintains her innocence. I have met with her over the years and am very proud of her health advocacy efforts on behalf of the women living behind bars. She relates the grim circumstances they face and the lack of humane treatment for dire medical conditions such as AIDS and COVID-19.

Inspired by aunt Dorothy and all her passionate work I worked for many years with incarcerated women who navigate living with HIV and/or AIDS.

Now I am a certified HIV/AIDS Peer Counselor through the New York State Department of Labor and the AIDS Institute and I took particular interest in the early reports about COVID-19 when it first appeared in the news.

Because I am well aware of how quickly novel viruses can spread, I was deeply concerned about this new threat as it was eerily reminiscent of the early days of HIV. In a matter of months, I found myself, much like the rest of the world, shocked by the rapid spread of the COVID-19 pandemic. And I was living in New York, right in the epicenter of it all. However, unlike most of the world, I was, and still am, living in a maximum-security prison.

While the world was being told to wear masks, we had none. While the world was being told to practice social distancing, we could not. While the world was being told to use hand sanitizers, we had none. While the world was being told to use antibacterial soap, I knew I lived among women who could barely afford soap, let alone be choosy about what kind.

The prison responded to this new disease by locking us in our cells to force social distancing. However, that meant no one could watch the news. I frantically followed news reports on ABC AM radio. I left my radio on that station 24 hours a day and yelled out news updates to the other women on my corridor. I passed on information about symptoms, treatments, and positive cases, sadly even mounting death counts as days passed.

When Governor Andrew Cuomo began giving daily briefings, I relayed his messages to the women on my housing unit. This was an incredibly frightening time as every day we would hear about women from our housing unit, or other housing units, who were sick, and went over to the hospital and were kept there.

We knew they likely had COVID-19 but we also heard they had run out of beds in the infirmary and were housing multiple sick women in the same rooms. Since the prison had stopped all visitors and civilian staff from entering the prison months before, our only contact with anyone who could pass on the virus would be the correction officers who work here. Some women exhibiting symptoms on the housing units were being stigmatized by others, which also reminded me of the same type of stigmatization that people with HIV suffer.

I constantly had to remind others that any of us could be subject to contracting the same virus at any given moment in these closed quarters, and that we all needed to spread love and support rather than judgment and division. When we were able to get out to use the phones, I worked with advocacy groups, task forces, churches, and people I know who were sympathetic and generous and asked them to get us donations of antibacterial soap.

With help from others. I was able to acquire masks and hand sanitizers, which we eventually got months later. I pleaded with everyone to advocate for the testing of all high-risk groups of inmates, including those with HIV/AIDS, Hepatitis, Lupus, Diabetes, Asthma, the elderly, and so on.

Sadly, to this day, that still has not happened here. While we did have many positive cases, the good news is, that the vast majority of the women who had COVID have recovered and have returned to the population to live among us. Yet, we had one woman who died from complications and her passing has deeply affected all of us here.

Today, we remain in the same forced-social-distancing lockdown, where we are only permitted to leave our cells for a few hours a day. The emotional and psychological effects have been debilitating, especially for the large portion of our population who already suffer from mental illnesses such as depression and anxiety. I find myself doing the same thing I did when confronted with the horror and devastation of AIDS, and that was, and is, to pray, for both a cure and until there is one, our resiliency.

In this next section I share the views, experiences and recollections of many individuals who recall their organization or personal work in the early years of HIV/AIDS. They share how the groundwork was laid for the AIDS Drug Assistance Program, how the program became the critically needed go-to resource for this vulnerable population, and how, against all odds and often much resistance, their innovative tactics and strategies made it all work.

SUDDENLY, GOOD NEWS
LAUNCHES A NEW APPROACH

Gregg S. Gonsalves, PhD

As Assistant Professor Yale School of Public Health and Co-Director, Global Health Justice Partnership, Gregg S. Gonsalves, PhD has worked on HIV/AIDS and other global health issues for more than 30 years. He also became involved with the AIDS Coalition to Unleash Power (ACT UP); the Treatment Action Group; Gay Men's Health Crisis and the AIDS and Rights Alliance for Southern Africa. He is a 2018 MacArthur Fellow.

In 1996, at the 3rd Conference on Retroviruses and Opportunistic Infections in Washington, D.C., Abbott Laboratories, showed the results of a pivotal study on ritonavir, one of the new generations of AIDS drugs called the protease inhibitors. We in the audience were impressed. This data showed that in just six months, those people receiving ritonavir plus Standard Of Care (SOC) had 50% fewer deaths than those receiving placebo plus SOC.

This was a watershed event in the history of the pandemic and represented the shift of AIDS from a death sentence to a chronic manageable illness. However, there was now something new to consider. For those of us in the Treatment Action Group having been so focused on drug development and drug approval for so long, this new success story now posed a new challenge: how to get the drugs to those who needed them most.

Back in the mid 1990s, with the collapse of the Clinton healthcare initiative, people with HIV without employer-based healthcare or were already ineligible for Medicaid had few avenues to gain access to these life-saving drugs.

Enter the ADAP Working Group, which had been formed for this very task to get the Congress to appropriate funds for a program to ensure these medicines were available in the U.S. regardless of insurance status.

Remember: healthcare expansion had gone down in flames in the first Clinton Administration, but the ADAP Working Group had convinced Congress to pass the Ryan White CARE Act and appropriate funds to support access to AIDS care and treatment. It was a remarkable achievement and democratized access to these new therapies.

While disparities and inequities in healthcare still exist to this day, ADAP was a lifeline for tens of thousands of people living with HIV and without insurance or other ways to pay for these drugs. I was one of those people and was on New York State and Connecticut ADAP programs on and off through the years since then.

WITNESSING THE TURNING
OF THE TIDE

Thad Zajdowicz, MD. MPH

Thad Zajdowicz, MD, MPH, is an HIV/AIDS Physician at the forefront of the early days and he has kindly allowed us permission for his personal artwork to be included on the cover.

In 1985, as a young infectious disease physician in the Navy, I was tasked with forming an HIV Evaluation Unit for sailors and Marines who tested positive for HIV infection. My wife and I ran that unit for the next ten years, evaluating more than 2500 mostly young, mostly male people.

The first five years of that experience were the absolute worst. With no effective treatment for the underlying HIV infection, we struggled to help our patients fight opportunistic infections and cancers with the horrible knowledge that death was always the inevitable and ultimate outcome. With the advent of antivirals and finally, the understanding that they needed to be used almost like cancer chemotherapy we began at last to turn the tide.

Nonetheless, we remain haunted decades later by what our young patients endured. All who were known to have this disease suffered a condemning scorn no less than that of a thousand years earlier among people with plague who were shunned, stoned and reviled. Despite 20th century enlightenment, the victories of science had done little to alter public attitude to the unknown. The devastating effects of immediate and widespread condemnation toward people affected created an embedded stigma that lingers today, decades later.

A REVEALING GLIMPSE BEHIND THE CORPORATE CURTAIN

William Schuyler

The observations and recollections from William Schuyler, Vice President of Government Relations for GlaxoSmithKline are a window into a little-known world of this corporate environment. As an insider, Schuyler's personal journey in tandem with the advent of the ADAP Working Group is very revealing.

Given the difficulties of getting companies, AIDS advocates and HIV positive people to work together in a coalition, and under the lens of the most significant issues that had to be overcome, was an incredibly daunting task. These individuals that eventually became the ADAP Working Group had two primary goals. First, they needed to formulate a common purpose and then, agree to work together in cohesive willingness to actually build the necessary trust — both among themselves and with their intended audiences. Those two objectives, purpose and trust, were things that had to happen at the same time.

However, back then, there was this enormous distrust between the HIV/AIDS community and the drug manufacturers. If you were the HIV community you were desperate, you were pressuring anyone who would listen to take action. These folks were fighting against a wall of inertia and resistance.

But another factor compounding their progress was wide disagreement among the HIV advocacy community itself. They questioned whether the system was supporting them. For example, the most aggressive advocates chained themselves to the company headquarters the then-named Burroughs Wellcome, (now GSK) building. I think there was some concern in the patient community about where was Congress? Where was the Food

15

and Drug Administration? Where were the drug companies? Where was the healthcare system? Was it focused on them? There was concern about whether there was a path forward with the patient community that didn't create a disruptive theme that we couldn't manage, or we did not know how to respond to when it was happening.

Those initial communications between the groups were complicated and difficult to initiate. It is different for people with HIV, compared to populations with other medical diseases. Other patients have different sets of circumstances to contend with than patients with HIV.

So, for us, it was a learning curve, to figure out how to sit down, understand the entire picture. Only after that can you have the kind of conversations we did have. Only then are you equipped to building this kind of advocacy and find the place where you have a roadmap that is clear that says, "these are the set of things that are most important if we are going to address these problems."

The unknown realities of all that created distrust and they reacted as you might expect.

What we argued about most among ourselves was how would it be possible to find a place of collective consensus and direction that said, "We all think this is sufficiently important, and we all need to work together on it." And from there we can build a path where we know if we are going to work together on these things — and for that moment at least — we are not going to find ourselves at odds in some way or another.

Then from there, once we all agreed on this plan our next step was to agree that we would all go together to talk to Congress. In fact, we said we will go and talk to whoever we can get to listen, especially executives of large drug companies. And we will tell them all, "this is what we agree on." This was the right voice that would demonstrate unity and solidarity in purpose.

Plus, it was important to emphasize that after everyone says yes, we did stick to it.

Ultimately then, what the ADAP Working Group really did was allow enough of an opportunity for everybody to sit down in the same room and actually say, 'what is it we are trying to do?' And then hash it out. It didn't happen in a moment, but it happened over time. And actually, I was not surprised at the level of cooperation even though it took some time to build. Let's not forget what we were facing at the time. We think of AIDS differently now in the 21st century than we thought of AIDS then.

The other aspect was that there truly was real agreement within the larger community – whether you were a drug company, a hospital, a health care provider or a patient – in that we needed to support the entire CARE Act, and that ADAP was a part of Ryan White, not the other way around.

What was a focal issue for us was the agreement to make sure the CARE Act itself did not just become the AIDS Drug Assistance Program. The efforts performed by ADAPs had to be inserted as a line-item component into the CARE Act because the CARE Act was providing direct health care services, counseling services and other services. People needed to not only receive their medications but to benefit from all the ancillary services that the CARE Act made possible.

These programs addressed much more than just health issues, and each was crucial to this first-ever type of disease that demanded new thinking and new approaches. There was an education component. There was an access component. There was an anti-discrimination component. There were pieces of this that all needed to come together if you were going to take a patient population — which at that moment in time was in significant crisis — and then fix the system for them.

So, it was not mutually exclusive; ADAPs could not be the stand-alone programs. This insertion of ADAPs into Title II of the CARE Act was another of the well- thought out and important accomplishments of the ADAP Working Group.

I think looking back we were successful in building a system that actually said, "What does the world look like to the HIV patient in need?" and then, "How do you build a system that responds to that?" What was true about the Ryan White CARE Act is, it actually said, "Here are the realities of this patient population, and we are trying to figure out a way to fill every gap."

And how gratifying to think that across the country, pretty much everywhere you went, if you were an HIV positive patient you could go into a clinic somewhere and get the care you needed. Again, this was due, in part, to the leadership efforts of that ADAP Working Group.

Then, when GSK developed the concept of combination therapies with AZT and 3TC this created the first real moment of genuine hope. This was the point that turned the corner. It was this "transformative technology" that I called it, that took a diagnosis of HIV from a death sentence to one of a chronic condition and changed the course for millions of patients. The addition of protease inhibitors was the transformative piece of this chapter.

Now, before the advent of these combination therapies and protease inhibitors, ADAPs covered few medications. But then, with the introduction of the combination therapies, the need to fund ADAPs became ever more critical.

We knew already that going out to agencies and government and asking for money must always be accompanied by evidence that illustrates the irrefutable proof it is needed. So, to help us do that, Bill Arnold, Co-chair of the ADAP Working Group contracted with a university to run a pharmacoeconomic model to determine the economic value of the ADAP investment. In other words, he could show with statistical evidence and hard data that when these drugs are paid for, here is how patients benefit, here is how the system can avoid the medical expenses arising from lack of medicine, and here's how society benefits from those coverages as well, when people are healthy they can keep their job and a sustainable lifestyle. It was just the ticket we needed; figures we could take to the financial sources and for them to say, "yes, we see the value," and to then open their wallets.

We had also sought to make sure that whatever government programs were out there were fully utilized, and there was no waste. And we as a drug company stepped up and said, "if there are waiting lists, we will provide free drugs to people on waiting lists." It was the ethical thing to do, and I am proud we acted in this responsible manner.

Aside from that there were a whole range of patient assistance and other programs that we committed to and are today still committed to that enable people to stay with their therapies. I think at the time we believed that there was no one with the disease who was not getting treatment due to being on a program waiting list or waiting to qualify.

What history shows is that the well-designed infrastructure of the CARE Act changed from a program designed to help people die with dignity, to a program that enabled people to live. We didn't talk about it that way at the time, but that is what we did.

But in the end, one of our successes was making sure we put patients back in the center of this conversation. By collaborating we were able to build a sustainable model that is operating today and enables people with a disease that at one point was going to kill them to live a normal life. That is its enduring value.

I think we also did a good job of demystifying HIV which at the time was essential. It is different today. But back then, there was still a lot of genuine fear around it. A drug company lobbyist and a patient with HIV can go present the issues together and talk about what the patient experience is and what is needed. I think in many ways these types of activities normalized the disease to be like any other disease, not this terrifying thing "we don't understand." And at the time, misunderstanding was hugely prevalent. And today even in some corners it sadly still is.

Perhaps we can say that ultimately, the most important lesson learned is that we need to hear the other person's point of view, and to recognize that the other person's point of view may not be communicable in five sentences. There needs to be a bit of understanding of where the patient is on this, and an understanding of how the system is responding, or in some cases not responding, to address that patient's needs.

Bill Arnold and Dorothy Keville were both critical in all these efforts, and in marshaling people together. They had a knack and insight combined with the ability to actually say, "this is a disease like no other so we must go out there and talk about what this patient population needs." They were able to convey the facts and the reality that action is necessary because this is a disease, not because HIV is scary.

WORKING TOGETHER TO LOWER AIDS DRUG PRICES

Julie M. Scofield, Founding Executive Director of NASTAD, 1993-2015

The cost of AIDS drugs back then was simply too high for states to cover. To set ground rules on who would be eligible to get free HIV drugs states implemented drug formularies — a list of approved drugs, generic and branded — that they would make available. With 50+ separate programs across the country they were difficult to administer and with no national unifying policy it made for much inconsistency. Julie was at the inception of NASTAD whose mission to organize the system and create a unified voice became the standard bearer of drug negotiation. Her work with others illustrates what happens when 'there is a will there is a way.'

The National Alliance of State and Territorial AIDS Directors (NASTAD) was founded in 1993, and its mission is to harness the collective voices of State Health Department AIDS Directors to influence the direction of federal AIDS policy and funding. By that time in the early '90s every state had a senior health department official charged with developing statewide systems of prevention and care for people living with AIDS using the state and federal funds that were available. With the first federal funding for the AZT program in the early 1990s, states began developing programs that were specifically designed for increasing access to treatment.

With passage of the Ryan White CARE Act, the state AIDS Drug Assistance Programs were created as a component through Title II. As the number of drugs to treat AIDS increased, and particularly with the advent of protease inhibitors in the mid-1990s, these programs became increasingly important as a critical lifeline for people with HIV. Because NASTAD represented state AIDS directors and ADAP programs, our annual data collection and monitoring of the ADAP programs was the critical backbone of advocacy efforts. This data was used as evidence to convince members of Congress to give us money, plus it was always important to remind policymakers at the state level that there were also federal funds.

One of the critical factors of historical importance to the story of ADAPs was the creation of the ADAP Crisis Task force. This was created in 2002 by a group of state AIDS and ADAP directors concerned about the nationwide fiscal crisis facing ADAPs. So, in March 2003, NASTAD provided logistical support for the first Task Force negotiation sessions between representatives from the ten largest ADAP programs and the eight companies that manufactured antiretroviral (ARV) drugs.

The goal of that first meeting was to obtain significant and multi-year concessions on HIV/AIDS drug prices for all ADAPs. Following the initial negotiations, agreements were reached with all eight manufacturers which we considered a spectacular achievement.

Since then, the Task Force has continued its work, extending the original agreements as well as negotiating when new drugs are approved by the Food and Drug Administration (FDA).

Additional agreements with companies that manufacture medications for HIV-related conditions have also been secured. We could report that the work we did in collaborating with manufacturers had reduced ADAPs' antiretroviral costs by $338 million in 2015 and is a benchmark as one of the most innovative initiatives in the history of public health. To date, the cumulative savings of Task Force agreements exceed $3 billion and demonstrates what can be accomplished through goodwill negotiations between state government representatives and the pharmaceutical industry.

I am gratified to share in the telling of what is truly a little-known chapter in the HIV/AIDS story. The legacy is measured in the countless lives extended and saved though access to life-saving medicine.

HOUSING OPPORTUNITIES
FOR PEOPLE WITH AIDS

Michael Montgomery, Former Chief, Office of AIDS, California
Department of Health Services; Former California ADAP Director

Knowing when and how to bring people together was Michael's great sense of timing. He gathered those he respected to brainstorm a new way to get funding and negotiate so that all states could benefit by 'making the pie bigger.'

In 1985 I helped set up an AIDS program in a rural county in California and then assisted in organizing the HOPWA, (Housing Opportunities for People with AIDS), program. This was just before the combination therapies took off and the ADAP program exploded. Then in 1994 I became the AIDS Branch Chief, and in that role, I supervised the ADAP director.

Before I got involved with the ADAP Working Group and the ADAP Crisis Task Force, I would have told you that the whole concept of public/private partnerships was kind of a joke. But what I found with the ADAP Working Group, and even more so with the ADAP Crisis Task Force, was how effective it was when there was collaboration with advocates, government and industry.

There were people within all of those big, international corporations who genuinely cared about the program, and helped us to make this work. Dorothy Keville was a good example of someone who came out of industry and cared about what we were doing.

I also recall how the pharmaceutical companies in collaboration with the ADAP Working Group, funded the annual ADAP Educational Forums in Washington, D.C. The Working Group coordinated these conferences and what was unique about them is how they brought together ADAP directors representing programs of all sizes to share issues and ideas.

Before the ADAP Crisis Task Force came into being New York ADAP Director Lanny Cross talked to me several times about how we needed to organize and negotiate for lower prices for AIDS drugs. Lanny was very adamant that while New York and California had substantial leverage on their own and any organization that was put together had to be a national effort and a voice for the entire country so that we could use our collective power to negotiate lower prices.

What we did was set up a meeting in San Diego and invited directors from the eight largest ADAPs to talk about a strategy. Lanny and several others organized that agenda. Murray Penner represented NASTAD and was critical in getting NASTAD and Julie Scofield to agree to handle the logistics of a negotiating task force. Ultimately, we forged the ADAP Crisis Task Force which became the negotiator for drug rebates. Now we were ready to set up meetings for negotiation.

The first one was in Washington, DC. We lined up four or five companies, and over two days or so we worked on getting better prices. Over time it was outrageously successful. According to Murray Penner, the ADAP Crisis Task Force saved states a half a billion dollars through the drug rebate program.

However, at that time when we started everyone was taking three or four drugs at a time. and many states, particularly the southern states, had to start waiting lists and shut the programs down. In that era, due directly to the ADAP Crisis Task Force and drug rebate programs we had initiated, we were able to really make a huge difference.

The ADAP Crisis Task Force was created at a critical moment — in the midst of programs shutting down, the beginning of waiting lists and states taking drugs off their formularies. We were however, also mobilized by this. 'This is an immediate crisis, people are going to die. We have to do something,' we thought. But the concept of negotiation, such as would be the role of the Task Force, was not new — this is what pharmacy benefit management corporations do every day. Medicaid programs, for example, negotiate for lower drug prices – lower than those mandated by law, so it was already being done.

But this was the first-time states got together – banded together – and negotiated together, we were almost like a trade union organizer. Other organizations were very aware of how well the ADAP Programs were doing in arguing for lower drug prices. When I retired there were about 30,000 people on the California ADAP program.

My recollection from these times also brings to mind how there was a huge push in Congress to increase the amount of funding for the Ryan White CARE Act and the ADAP programs. Before the combination therapies, the ADAP program handled a surge from 7,000 to 8,000 patients to 30,000 patients and the ADAPs went from being a sideline story to being a big program under the Ryan White CARE Act. Individual states like mine, California, also contributed to ADAP programs. The pressure was really enormous to fund the ADAP program.

In what we would now call a blue state, the funding increased exponentially. But it was pressure from external sources – the people who were living with AIDS and HIV — who really demanded that those programs be fully funded. They were very effective influencing the California legislature and also the United States Congress. I think California went from a program of $8 million to a program of $17 million within months and it wasn't easy. In California, we had a responsive government that listened. We had a Republican administration, and they recognized this was an emergency.

On one occasion, when we had a hearing in California, literally hundreds of people who were living with HIV showed up. Plus we had representatives from advocacy organizations like Project Inform, AIDS Project Los Angeles, the San Francisco AIDS Foundation, and New York's Gay Men's Health Crisis. All of these voices exerted enormous pressure to get funding on the state and federal levels.

It was so different than it is now. People were dying and I had a lot of friends die in 1994, but within just a year, you had combination therapies. The change was just so dramatic.

24

We literally thought, "If they just could have lived a few months longer and had access to the combination therapies." The drug companies were really aware that funding was necessary both for their product and for people to live. One example was that GlaxoSmithKline gave California a retroactive rebate of $3 million in 1994 to help expand our formulary, which we were able to do. They were certainly aware that this would mean we would be able to add drugs to our formulary.

Once when I was traveling to Washington, D.C. and I was at O'Hare International Airport in Chicago, a Republican Congressman from California was on my flight. He was sitting in the boarding area and since I never wanted to miss an opportunity, I went over to him and started cajoling him about funding for ADAP. His response was, "Where are you going to get the money? Where are you going to take the money from?" He was saying, "We are not going to add money. We are going to have to take money from somewhere else or we are not going to have money." That was the kind of thinking they had, and it was a problem.

Then the question became who is getting too big a piece of the pie. The congressional delegation from California, New York and from Massachusetts agreed the solution was "let's make a bigger pie."

Without support from their congressional delegations for additional funding, however, the Southern states and smaller states worked from the perspective of how to cut up the existing pie. But the ADAP Crisis Task Force wanted to make sure everybody got what they needed. That was where the big challenge was.

Then there was the sticky issue of how the Medicaid regulations were written. People who had HIV but not AIDS were not eligible for Medicaid. This created a legislative paradox because they couldn't get the medications to prevent them from developing AIDS, and then when they did develop AIDS, they would become Medicaid eligible. It was a kind of perverse logic.

The point is, at that time you wanted people to get what they needed to control HIV and prevent them from progressing to AIDS.

I have always felt I am not a great leader, and I don't have great ideas and I am not a public health professional. But I have a real sense of timing — who can do what and who can work together. I was able to get people together at the right time and this is what we did with the ADAP Crisis Task Force which I credit as my proudest accomplishment. I absolutely credit Lanny Cross with the idea of negotiating for lower drug prices. I don't think the contribution Lanny made will ever be adequately acknowledged for how critical he was to the ADAP program nationally, directly helping to save thousands of lives. Murray Penner deserves huge kudos for getting NASTAD to believe in doing this and supporting us. Then there was Dwayne Haught of Texas who was a force to be reckoned with.

The legislature could argue that they were part of the solution – that they were holding a tough line with the private corporations. They were saying, "We are paying for these drugs, but you have to come in with rebates." Yes, the drug companies came up with a product to save lives. but we took a program and enhanced it, and enlarged it, literally saving thousands of lives and people are alive today because that program was available.

There is no question that the enduring legacy of the ADAP Crisis Task Force are lives saved!

LEARNING TODAY FROM YESTERDAY'S MISTAKES

James Driscoll, PhD, Author of

How AIDS Activists Challenged America & Saved FDA from Itself

Jim Driscoll was a member of the ADAP Working Group that helped with his contacts in the FDA which was an important component providing the Group with updated information about the drug approval process. He navigated conflicts among AIDS activist groups as they struggled with both political parties to be heard and respected.

Dorothy Keville like many of the most valuable AIDS activists, is an unusual person of many talents that turned out to be badly needed once she had found her niche. But "badly needed" is an understatement for Dorothy's role in founding the ADAP Working Group and coordinating between a raucous unwieldy community and a rigid industry not used to street activism – here Dorothy was indispensable. Had she not been in the right place at the right time to speed the implementation of the new AIDS cocktails, many lives would have been needlessly lost. What made Dorothy indispensable was not only her long experience working with the community, industry and government, but her peculiar diplomatic tact and grace coupled with just the right amount of charm or iron as was needed to get life-saving drugs to those who needed them.

Much has been written comparing the coronavirus epidemic with the

1918 flu that killed an estimated 675,000 U.S. citizens, about the same number as those who have died from AIDS. During the AIDS epidemic, the Food and Drug Administration was a crucial factor, as it is now. So, the mistakes the FDA made with the AIDS epidemic can be instructive today if we are willing to learn from them.

WAITING LISTS TO BECOME ELIGIBLE TO RECEIVE TREATMENT

Murray Penner, NASTAD

Waiting lists were created in many of the states as the only recourse when they ran out of money. Under a certain ruling called 340B, states were limited on what they could provide in terms of support for AIDS medicines, but Murray Penner from NASTAD was instrumental in finding ways to help states cope. His efforts helped in coordination of the AIDS Crisis Task Force.

My work with ADAPs began in 2001 when I joined the National Alliance of State and Territorial AIDS Directors in Washington. I remember the first assignment was to work with Bill Arnold from the ADAP Working Group on tracking state ADAP waiting lists. At the time, demand for antiretrovirals far exceeded federal funding and there was limited state funding.

Our ADAP Monitoring Report, in conjunction with the Kaiser Family Foundation had been involved tracking funding and utilization because HHS's Health Resources and Services Administration was not tracking this information at that time. A big part of this initiative was also tracking waiting lists.

Then in 2002, Michael Montgomery, the State AIDS director from California, and Lanny Cross, the ADAP director for the State of New York, summoned me to San Diego for a meeting. Also present were representatives from other ADAP programs including North Carolina, Massachusetts, Maryland, and Texas. Lanny and Michael had an idea, hatched literally on the back of a napkin during a happy hour that would address the unacceptable ADAP waiting lists. Their idea was to create a

Task Force whose role would be to meet with industry partners to get pricing concessions on HIV medications.

I was skeptical, but I agreed, with support from Julie Scofield and NASTAD to go forward to organize people and set up meetings with industry partners. And thus, the ADAP Crisis Task Force was born in 2003. In early 2003, the first group of eight AIDS and ADAP directors from the four biggest states — New York, California, Texas and Florida — met with ALL of the eight pharmaceutical companies that were manufacturing HIV medications.

The overarching founding principles were to persuade companies that they needed to invest ethically and financially and motivate them to be part of the solution to ending ADAP waiting lists. The first goal was to obtain significant and multiyear concessions on HIV/AIDS drug prices for all ADAPs. Our first agreement was with Roche and I started to believe that it would work. I believe our last agreement was with GlaxoSmithKline. But it was a time of many tense discussions and high drama, and I even remember one company representative walking in with a large check for NASTAD, hoping that would help convince us to come to an easy agreement. But it didn't work – we did NOT accept the check. Then another company could not travel internationally due to the beginning of the war in Iraq, so we conducted that negotiation by phone.

By the end of 2003, we had reached agreements with all eight manufacturers. The Task Force and agreements still continue today, the inarguable force in ending ADAP waiting lists in about 2010.

The real story about the ADAP Crisis Task Force is that many lives, probably hundreds of thousands have been saved and improved as a result of Michael and Lanny's vision and the tenacity of the Task Force.

Furthermore, the industry partners were very integral as partners in making this happen - by providing significant concessions on ARV prices. It truly is a partnership that saved lives then and now — and has been an untold story about the success of public-private partnerships and dedication of many public health officials in saving lives.

GREATEST PUBLIC HEALTH CHALLENGE OF OUR TIME

Lanny Cross, New York ADAP Manager

New York was in the forefront of the crisis along with California. One of the most knowledgeable leaders in this arena was New York's Lanny Cross whose savvy in navigating bureaucratic hurdles and bringing states together to help each other administer their programs was legendary. Every HIV/AIDS conference that had a program featuring a session with his latest endeavors was filled to capacity with people anxious to learn what he was doing in New York. He was a mentor to all his counterparts and says, "It was the greatest public health challenge of our time."

When I first came on, we were running the whole program ourselves, so innovation was the standard operating procedure. At first, we only had AZT and it caused a lot of toxicity. Moreover, when people were coming into care, they already had symptoms and their immune system was gone, so even with medicine it was still a death sentence.

Over time there was an administrative and activist push to the medicalization of AIDS, so low -income people who had more resources could now be served by Medicaid. But we had to be vigilant in working around bureaucratic hurdles that restricted how money could be spent. One of the ways we solved this problem was by leveraging our Health Department's not-for-profit agency partner. That way we could circumvent and bypass restrictions.

One example of this novel thinking is during my first year with ADAP we had $12M in one-time funding but had only spent $2M. Typically, if you don't spend your allocation, you won't get it again but there were so many things we could do, and we did them.

31

I came up with ways to expand the program and created telephone hotlines, hired People With AIDS (PWAs) for staffers and people from the gay lesbian community. We did outreach and began a subway poster campaign to increase awareness and worked with the AIDS Coalition to Unleash Power (ACT UP).

While we were working with HIV activists who had educated themselves, the general public remained pretty fearful. There were no end to horror stories of landlords throwing tenant's stuff out on the street, families disowning their children. Then in 1995 new combination therapies were working and people's CD4 white blood count shot up; their immune system became reconstituted.

All at once we were seeing miracles. Our friends got up off their deathbed when they were just weeks away from dying, that's how dramatically the new drugs had impact. The death rate dropped by 85% so now with these success stories in hand we had something to work with. This was the perfect evidence for us to start educating and lobbying for more money for ADAP.

Crucially, a few key people led primarily by Dorothy Keville had pulled together a group of drug company executives and activists — the traditional adversaries — but this meeting was designed to sensitize manufacturers and then subsequently lawmakers. It worked.

ADAP enrollment skyrocketed and we finally had a good story to tell. The media was all over it – Time, Newsweek, the New York Times were all reporting these miracles – and any legislator working on budgets saw the program was working and could support it. In looking back, it really was an era of both the worst of times and the best of times, but I was there when there was no hope and death was the daily news, and I was still there when we could be reporting miracles.

I am so gratified I could play a role and witness this.

OVERCOMING OBSTACLES WITH COMMUNITY PARTNERS

Christine Rivera, New York State ADAP Director

Chris was so committed to overcoming any obstacles that her leadership and engaging personality made it easier to talk about safe sex and share the message of Undetectable Means Untransmittable (U=U).

Being gay myself, I felt a personal responsibility to get involved in the AIDS epidemic. Friends were dying in droves from this disease due to misinformation that fueled the morbidity fires.

During the early years of the epidemic virtually everyone who was involved in the policy, care, prevention and treatment of people living with HIV/AIDS were motivated to do that work because of a personal connection.

When I first came to the ADAP office in 1990 it was during the Reagan administration and our efforts to provide access to care were hamstrung by conservative Republican attitudes and power. For example, the Republican governor of New York would not allow the word sex to be used in any HIV/AIDS prevention efforts, and with half of the nation's epidemic in New York the consequences of that policy were devastating. I truly believe the political ideology of the early days of the epidemic fueled the increase in cases and spawned an environment of social and political apathy. The legacy of that era persists unfortunately, even today.

Stigma and discrimination have become so entrenched in our value system that even now, so many decades and so many treatment advances later, people with HIV/AIDS still face overt and profound prejudices in every aspect of their lives. In 2020 while I was out to dinner with acquaintances, when they asked me what I did for a living, I still get "that look," from presumably enlightened and socially responsible individuals. It's almost like they want to move their chair back ... "ya know ... just in case."

I remember how the restraints from the political arena had an effect on our community and what could or could not be implemented. Because of those political handcuffs under which we had to work in those early years, we engaged our community partners as the megaphone to spread safe sex and treatment option messages throughout the state. They became our voice in the field across city, urban, small town and rural areas throughout a large, diverse state spreading the word about care, treatment and prevention.

During the early 90s the antiretroviral drugs we had to "treat" HIV/AIDS had horrific side effects, yet our participants were grateful they had affordable access to anything that could help ease their disease and help manage their symptoms. Now, because of the progress we have made in the past 26 years, over half of the ADAP population today is over age 50, which means not only are they successfully managing an ongoing infectious disease they are also growing older. There was a time when this was unthinkable and you were happy to just reach your next birthday. The future of viral suppression continues to evolve and improve and in the not-too-distant future we will see a very different treatment game with long-acting antivirals.

I think the history of how far we have come, and the terrible years so many endured is not known to younger people. It's important for them to understand how we got where we are and to continue to use their voices to make sure everyone knows their status and seeks care and prevention options sooner, rather than later.

The science has given us this formula U=U, which is "Undetectable means Untransmittable," which helps remove the stigma associated with living with HIV and the personal pariah feeling. Hopefully this message will be resonating into the future.

After more than three decades of this work I am continually amazed I lasted as long as I did and now, as I go into retirement, I cannot overstress this message to ADAP directors: Be kind to yourself, you are doing amazing and challenging work.

AIDS IN NORTH DAKOTA - OVERCOMING THE CHALLENGE OF DISTANCE

Denise Steinbach, North Dakota ADAP Director

Despite long distances, few providers, and even fewer specialists, plus inherent stigma and discrimination, Denise was able to convince an oil refinery to contribute much-needed assistance. The industry giant responded willingly by donating gas cards that enabled the critical travel allowing medical staff to visit and treat patients across North Dakota.

At 500 miles from west to east and not much in between, distance in our state presented a challenge. Not only are facilities far flung across the state, we had low numbers of cases, so people were really not talking about HIV. And they also were not talking about gay men. We only had 10 cases a year in 1999 and awareness to the facts and science of the condition in the public community was still limited.

However, we began to see that stigma and fear was lessening due to public education programs, but our health department program still had only one non-physician and one medical officer. These folks were so incredibly dedicated and between the two of them they were always thinking about what they could do, what would be the best thing for people. They wanted to make sure our drug formulary would be as complete as it could be, plus there were only three infectious disease doctors in the whole state.

Despite these challenges there are some notable efforts I am very proud to be a part of. First, we had an oil refinery in Bismarck. We approached them and told them how some of our clients had to drive hours just to see a doctor in the capitol, and that our doctors had to travel extensive distances to visit Indian reservations and treat tribal people. The folks there were great and asked how many gas cards we needed and then made that donation to literally help keep the program services on the road. They did not want transportation to be a barrier to treatment.

Another key part was getting and keeping people engaged in the programs we had so we brought in Persons With AIDS (PWAs) from the community to help us. They monitored the chat rooms and were able to put out a lot of prevention messages. It was great advocacy as this one-on-one also allowed the people to hear what someone was facing and they could say, "Well, let me tell you my story." It was a very personal intervention.

But because of our state's geography and far-flung services we wanted to do more. So, to cover a lot more ground one of the PWA's agreed to be an actor for a 30 second video spot that our department broadcast on TV and radio. Our goal to reach a lot of people who would otherwise have no clue how to access our services was simple: use the air waves. One PWA guy did a TV spot for us and the whole point of it was to convey that HIV is treatable; it doesn't have to be a death sentence, and you can live a full life if you get on the right medication. This medium let us reach thousands who might otherwise have remained unaware of their options to access care and treatment.

We also have a lot of tribal people here with about 20,000 living on reservations and another 16,000 off-reservation. They had an even harder time getting health care and treatment for HIV/AIDS back then: it was so complicated with the state and tribal hierarchies. Providers working in tribal health are really stretched thin as they are day-to-day focused on diabetes, heart disease, nutrition, and respiratory issues that are so prevalent among this population.

Today looking back, it was such a struggle just to see case managers who were dealing with so many issues. It would sometimes take hours to travel to see patients and people were often afraid. I always said, it doesn't matter how you got HIV, don't be afraid, you can get help.

It was the most fulfilling work of my career and brings back so many memories. It was difficult, but so rewarding. I was doing something important, and I could see how I made a difference in their lives.

MANAGING THE FINANCES - AIDS IN WEST VIRGINIA

Jay Adams, West Virginia Part B and ADAP Coordinator

Determined to help educate anyone in the 'Bible belt conservative' state, Jay Adams in West Virginia had his work cut out for him. He recalls how in that environment, people facing the prospect of telling family members they were gay was more frightful than having them learn they had AIDS.

All I ever wanted to do from the first day was make a difference in the lives of people living with AIDS. I wanted them to have less chaos; feel a little better without the worry of wondering whether they would get the relief they needed.

When the State tapped me to take over a new program for AIDS medication, I was the only employee and had no guidance and I literally had to start from scratch figuring out enrollment, the pharmacy and provider involvement and of course, managing the finances of the program. But at that time when I got involved, I was already working a full-time job, plus volunteering in helping young gay men who had been diagnosed and had come back to the area. This was a huge volunteering commitment of sometimes 40 hours a week.

The things I heard and witnessed were devastating. So many of them were shunned; their families isolated them, insisting they had to eat off Styrofoam plates and sleep separately from the rest of the family. Most of them never saw their friends again. Because of this my goal was to educate people, which now in looking back, has really become my life legacy to this arena that I am so proud of having contributed.

It was in my coping with this 'Bible belt conservative,' that really motivated me to embrace the role of an educator across all arenas. It was stunning to see how my clients were far more afraid to tell people — especially their family members — they were gay, than it was to tell them they had AIDS. And they lived in fear on a daily basis of losing those important supports and having to be demoralized again and again as their family members would follow them around the house, wiping down surfaces with Clorox wipes, washing their clothes and dishes in different batches. But it was the isolation that I think might have been the worst. The families isolated their children from church and any social interaction; it was terrible.

Yet, awful as it was, I could understand that they were doing all of this out of fear, and from lack of information and from not understanding what this disease was all about, and then you put this under the lens of long held conservative traditions and beliefs and it's a disaster.

So, my work in teaching and spreading the word about the facts of HIV was cut out for me from day one.

If you haven't spent any time in my state, you wouldn't realize how geographically challenging everything was. From remote areas in the mountains and valleys to long stretches between towns, trying to coordinate across the network of providers in a state like West Virginia is a fairly heroic undertaking. But I did arrange things with caregivers.

One thing we did was talk to nursing schools. I worked with providers and especially social workers who did discharge planning at hospitals. Our office had developed a brochure about the ADAP program, and we got it into the hands of as many groups as possible so they would be aware of our services. Plus, it was very important to get into the churches, especially the black churches as people really listen to their pastor.

Overcoming the ever-present undercurrent of fear that people would be rejected, that their family wouldn't love them anymore was very real. It was heartbreaking to have to even find funeral directors who would take people and would perform services. I had to be the go-between the family members and the client's partner who was often denied access at the end.

And for more than 300 people, I was there when they took their last breath. I sat at the bedside of the terminal people. holding their hands and offering comfort to the patient, their partner, and families.

I think that it is this one-on-one approach that makes the crucial difference — whether it was myself and a family member or an infectious disease physician and families. When people feel they are cared for and are important you can accomplish great things. I saw first-hand how that works.

AIDS IN FLORIDA -
STIGMA, DELAYS AND WEATHER

David Poole, Florida ADAP

Getting people in rural and urban areas the access to care and medicine, despite hurricanes and floods, is a major undertaking. But avoiding any lapses was, and still is a crucial key in managing disease, especially for people with HIV/AIDS. David recalls how he and his department in Florida had to cope with weather, insurance and other obstacles in order for people to continue having access to their medications and treatments.

It was 1993 and I remember being contacted by a fairly recent acquaintance, Judy Wray, who was the Program Administrator for the Ryan White Patient Care Program at what was then called the Florida Department of Health and Rehabilitative Services (HRS). Judy was interested in hiring me away from a local nonprofit AIDS Service Organization (ASO) to come and assist her with her program. I readily accepted and began a journey that would change my life forever!

I was hired initially to take a component of the Ryan White Program, AIDS Insurance Continuation, and implement that statewide, as it was then only available as a pilot in two counties at that time. Little did I know that this experience would introduce me to 67 county health departments. There was at that time in the early 90's a large statewide community of people living with HIV/AIDS that were constantly bombarded with barriers to care and treatment.

The overall Ryan White CARE Act program was federally funded and consisted of multi-jurisdictional parts that all fell under the purview of the respective governmental jurisdictions. It sounds complex and it was, but somehow, some way it all came together and worked quite well in those early days. People with HIV ultimately needed access to things they simply didn't have like insurance, treatment/medications, medical care, labs, case management, mental health and substance abuse counseling and on and on.

The mortality rates before 1996 were sky high as we didn't have very effective treatments – but what we did have was a large uninsured population in need of medications. And that is where the AIDS Drug Assistance Program (ADAP) came in. Ryan White funded this as a category of the state's overall award and it truly provided the only major access to antiretrovirals back then, and even to this day it is a major provider to people with limited or no access to needed medicines — especially in states that did not expand Medicaid.

In Florida, at the outset of Ryan White we made a major program decision to operate the ADAP through a central pharmacy purchasing model and we used the 67 County Health Departments (CHD's) as our points of access. In our minds, no matter how urban or how rural those agencies were, we were providing an important program to those in need. Using the system of existing CHD's was the bridge to getting these medications to people diagnosed with HIV, or, those who had progressed to AIDS.

I remember well how reliant patients became on this system and their medication access – but the one thing we had not counted on in terms of treatment interruption was hurricane prone Florida. I recall having to go into emergency preparation mode with staff, convening statewide calls before the storm for planning purposes and for ad-hoc reporting systems at a time where we didn't have near the sophistication we have today with weather forecasting, internet, and shipping systems to name a few.

During my tenure in Florida, I would hear directly from patients all over the state when systems failed and these clients were sometimes yelling at me about their personal dilemma and how to their way of thinking, their local health department didn't do something correctly. But we had a staff of no more than 15 or so who were running all statewide HIV care programs, and in these emergencies, we would have to shift responsibilities at the last minute to reassure the patients and the local providers that we would get their medications to them. And all the while a huge specter always hung over us that further compromised our efforts. And that was the specter of stigma and any violations in confidentiality of the patients' HIV status.

Much of the work we were doing was being replicated in states across the country but because of our diverse nation, each state ADAP often looked very different from the other. So, while it was always great to have a peer to go to it was not always helpful because of these differences, other than to have a sympathetic ear. One huge resource for all of us was the National Alliance of State and Territorial AIDS Directors (NASTAD). This organization was basically a trade group that represented the interests of all of the State HIV/AIDS Programs. NASTAD afforded us a powerful conduit of communication to tell our federal partners when things were going poorly, or when they were going well. It also provided us venues and conference call opportunities to work together on what was a very slippery and ever-changing landscape.

NASTAD was also responsible for ultimately leading to my love for advocacy around all things HIV but most especially in negotiating with big biotech and pharmaceutical companies that were providing us with effective new medications but at a staggering cost. I can remember coming together with California's HIV Director Michael Montgomery, New York's ADAP Director Lanny Cross and many others to hone our strategy with dealing with the good guys/bad guys. That led to many an interesting time at the restaurants and bars on Capitol Hill in DC where we would hold late night conversations and debates on what was the right thing to do.

I eventually crossed over to what my peers referred to as the "Darkside" when I joined Gilead Sciences pharmaceutical company in 2005. My 9 year journey with this industry was the best education I could ever receive on pharmaceuticals and the health care industry overall. I can also tell you it was my introduction into the excesses of the industry and how enormous and paradoxical the conflict is between innovation and capitalism! That being said, ADAP was a major customer of mine during my tenure at Gilead, and in fact I visited every health department and

ADAP in the nation at that time, which I feel gave me a very unique glimpse into the genius of the original authors of the 1990 Ryan White CARE Act.

That program which included ADAP, had provided a very unique solution to a one-of-a-kind challenge for a disease that emerged out of nowhere in 1981. It has now been 40 years since the first cases of HIV were diagnosed and we still have the Ryan White Program, and we still have ADAP. Is that a statement to its success or is it a testament to our failure? I do not have the answer.

After my nine-year stint working for Gilead Sciences and being introduced to a Government Affairs role, I left the company and joined the largest non-profit HIV organization in the world, AIDS Healthcare Foundation (AHF). In mid-2013 I was hired by the President, Michael Weinstein and Mike Kahane, Southern Bureau Chief to head up legislative affairs for the Southern States. This was truly a dream come true and it brought me back to my roots working for a non-profit devoted to the care and treatment of people living with HIV regardless of their ability to pay. The second portion of the AHF mission is devoted to advocacy as well and this is what really drew me to this organization. AHF has truly blazed a trail of overt in-your-face advocacy through amazing and provocative marketing campaigns aimed at stigma, hate, diversity and core public health principles.

Nonetheless, with success and growth comes criticism and acclaim; that same roller coaster ride exists still today, but in my mind that is the true measure you are making a difference. So, as is appropriate, I now advocate for many policy issues including ADAPs across the South. My goals are the relentless push for continued funding to improve their overall operations, and to best serve patients who are living quite well in most cases with a very treatable, mostly chronic, but manageable disease called HIV.

AIDS Healthcare Foundation is the largest Global AIDS organization delivering advocacy and support to over 1 million people in 43 countries. The organization brings skilled assistance to people with pharmacy and testing services, housing and educational information. (https://aidshealth.org)

MEANINGFUL CARE IN HAND HOLDING

Dwayne Haught, BSN, MSN, Texas ADAP Director

The dedicated nurses helping with HIV/AIDS provide a critical component to care found nowhere else, particularly in the early years. Their skilled and non-skilled caring done with compassion are what gets people through difficult times says nursing practitioner and Texas ADAP director, Dwayne Haught BSN, MSN and Certified AIDS Practitioner. He has unstinting praise for the often very difficult mission of nurses, particularly those working in AIDS, emphasizing their efforts are a vastly unrecognized and underrated contribution to the critical care and success of these patients.

Nurses don't receive enough acknowledgment for how important they are, and have been, in the care and treatments of patients, especially those with HIV/AIDS. And because they rely on science and facts, they are invaluable in helping educate on a personal level. As to my role in HIV/AIDS, events that ended up shaping my life began while I was an undergraduate student at the University of Miami, and during my nursing curriculum I worked at the Jackson Memorial Hospital, which is now the University of Miami University Hospital.

At the time I did know about HIV but the fact that the Hospital was doing a study on AZT and they were to break the code to understand the virus was a seminal moment. That hospital became the first to develop an HIV clinic and I am sure without exposure to that hospital my life might have taken a different turn. Jackson Memorial played an important role in the future of the disease and I was right there when that occurred.

Starting out, I worked as a nurse at an AIDS Services facility in

47

Austin, Texas where I did client and community education around AIDS, and we had some fund-raising to provide home care that was non-skilled but would help with just basic living.

It's hard to imagine now, in our current 21st century environment where we have so many treatment options, that at that time two and three decades ago, people were getting sick and dying so quickly. Their lives were immensely compromised, they couldn't shop for food, do simple chores like laundry, even bathing was an effort. For all of us in caregiving the challenges on every front were all new ones with this disease that was so unlike anything we had to face before. We had to learn all the basics of HIV/AIDS and we were creating knowledge on the fly for our efforts and developing strategies in how to best provide care. As fast as the science was evolving, we had to adapt and modify those efforts.

But most of all I remember how the people who were diagnosed with HIV had a huge burden beyond disease — concealing their status from family and friends, feeling defensive and marginalized by much of the medical community who in the face of this frightening, unfamiliar disease, often shied away from providing care. And they were angry at the manufacturers of medicines that were extraordinarily costly.

In 1990 when I first started, people were still dying pretty dramatically. When our clinic opened, we were serving about 200 people and by the time I left, ten years later, we had 2000 clients. The fact that people came to us in growing numbers was a reassurance that they had faith in what we were doing, that it was an OK place to go to.

As protease inhibitors were developed, along with other newer treatments, the death rate began to slow. People started to live. Nonetheless, it was still all very new territory, caring for people with this disease who were not going to die upon being diagnosed. There were still mistakes being made in HIV/AIDS treatment, but these could be averted if there was more informed caregiver decision making. So, I really saw myself in a leadership role to that end, and I went back to school to take a Masters degree in Nursing care. This was the tipping point for my being able to act as a community voice and spreading my health advocacy mission to a wide medical arena.

I was already a certified RN in HIV care but then I got a call one day asking if I could help develop a teaching component to the University of Texas nursing school. This would be for nurses who were on the frontline of patient care, but also at that time there was a huge problem with patient dental care. Dentists were refusing patients and we had to teach them how to accommodate HIV people.

The program was a spectacular success and in just three days we had 100 people sign up. Plus, the happy outcome of this project was our capacity to help reduce the stigma of this treatment from the dental and nursing profession. At about this same time I also took an interest in another underserved area which was women's health.

The majority of people at the time who were HIV positive were men, but there were some women, and they were really out in the cold so to speak, with nowhere to go or anyone who could adequately provide specialized care and education. I asked a colleague who was a female GYN physician to work with me and began the first women's clinic in Central Texas.

Now, my next pursuit was to start putting my specialty skills towards grant writing. By doing this I was useful in a different way but not run ragged mentally and emotionally each day.

Then, some nursing friends of mine asked me to help unsnarl the budgetary issues of the recently passed Texas ADAP. No one really knew how the medication program was going to work so I had to go to the legislature every two years to ask for money. It made the clients crazy as there was always the threat of being disenrolled if you were over the 200% poverty level. In 1987 it was $5,360 for 100% Federal Poverty Level. At 200% income would need to be below $10,720 to be eligible.

Then, I took on another first via the ADAP Task force — the group that typically negotiates the price for drugs and has the unenviable job of addressing manufacturers to plead the case for more money. This is something else that no one will remember, but at the time ADAP started and I took the job, nobody liked the program. The community was unhappy, it was very conservative in its financial eligibility, and acting like a formulary, it only allowed us to use FDA approved retrovirals. We didn't have anything to treat opportunistic infections, toxicities and no mental health drugs.

When I started as the ADAP Director we had 30 drugs and when I left there were 50, but even today, by most standards it is still inadequate. In 2011 there were some changes about the money that was specific to the Texas ADAP and the money spent could be counted as out of pocket costs for Medicare Part D, the infamous donut hole scenario.

So, then what happened as a result was we started getting rebates as we had opened a state pharmacy assisted program. Building that trust between this state government agency that was overshadowed with a conservative disposition, and the community we served took more than a year, and their attitudes ranged from belligerent to hostile. What I also learned, however, is that trust can be built if you build it on facts, not speculation.

To be effective and convincing I had to come with data and information to support the rationale of why we did what we did and demonstrate how our offerings to the community were based upon the realities of hard fact and data.

When you were in this from day one, as I was, and then look back through this history you have the advantage of seeing powerful transitions. One of the overarching observations is you see so many examples and situations where the stigma of this disease is alienating and isolating. Although we have come a long way it is still there, it still affects people and the negative effect is still very real, even in this enlightened age. This is underscored in the disparity of health outcomes with different groups who have HIV.

Most recently a significantly important example is the current debate over illegal people in this country, who out of fear of exposure, will avoid seeking treatment. This shines a glaring light on the negative effect of politics invading the arena of public health. My perspective over the decades is a lens to look back on those days when people first came to us and we learned new lessons from them, every day. The collective knowledge of this experience is that for me, going from seeing people dying in six months to now living a pretty normal life, is staggering.

I've lived through that transition and yet, despite this success, what has happened is that today I see an increasing complacence; HIV/AIDS has been put on the back burner and other issues like the opioid crisis, COVID-19 have taken center stage. But there are still many undiagnosed HIV cases, and it continues to spread. We are not done yet.

Just as we now are in reach of perhaps a cure, a vaccination and certainly the benefits of PrEP as a prevention, it should be getting more attention, not less. I feel lucky in that I can offer this vast repository of hands-on learning and I am always eager to pass it on to any and all who will listen.

I can truly say that my perspective from the earliest days to the 21st century is an extensive documentation of a unique moment in time, for HIV/AIDS people, for Texas public health history and for distinctive stories of the people I have encountered in those years.

At the time there was no ADAP staff, it was just me. I was taking people in, approving their eligibility, packing and shipping out medications, doing filing, handling phone calls, doing home visits, and coping with the never-ending government red tape. In some cases, I was sure I was probably breaking some law to just get the job done. Since it was only me and I was the only one, I did it all on the fly for the most part.

It wasn't a job — a job is 40 hours a week — this was a way of life, round the clock, every day of the year. In the end however, I have to say if you were open to this experience and open to life, this was a perilous and rocky journey to undertake. It was absolutely pioneering work. It was full of sadness, but it was also enriching to the person you were, and you were never the same if you embraced its challenges.

I've seen some people do it as a job for 40 hours a week, and today, with the hierarchy and administration and the latest technology it is a world away from what we did years ago. It's very different than stepping into the uncharted frontier journey that I took.

But what I can say is that it envelops you, and takes over much, if not all of your life. It wrecks some people, but somehow, I managed to get through it. Now, despite all that, I can say in complete honesty that my having done this enriched my life in a manner that I don't believe anything else would have, and my life was better because of it.

OFFERING A LIFELINE FOR LOW-INCOME PERSONS - AIDS IN ALABAMA

Kathie M Hiers, CEO, AIDS Alabama

Fighting the desperate scenario of policies whose data rewarded one group over another Kathie worked tirelessly to advance the message of equity for people with HIV/AIDS. Ensuring people had access to what they needed regardless of their status was her daily mission.

It would not be an understatement for me to say that the AIDS Drug Assistance Program component of the Ryan White law may be the most important piece of legislation enacted in the United States. It led directly to helping people living with HIV to live healthy, independent lives.

In the early days of HIV medications, particularly from 1996 forward, most people living with HIV could not afford the critical, life-saving prescriptions, which were quite expensive. It was the state-run ADAP that became a lifeline to low-income persons who so desperately needed the antiretroviral medications to stay alive. But as is the case with most statutes, the Ryan White CARE Act was imperfect.

Understandably, during its original genesis, emphasis and funding had been concentrated in the urban areas, especially the bicoastal cities, as those were the jurisdictions hardest hit initially by the HIV epidemic. But as the epidemic moved inexorably forward into the southern United States and into rural America, the law and the funding were not flexible enough to move with the epidemic into the new epicenter of HIV/AIDS, the American South, which is my familiar territory.

In the early 1990s, a group of AIDS Directors from the South formed a new group to address these inequities. We had leaders from North Carolina, Louisiana, Florida, Tennessee, who formed a group of Southern AIDS Directors using the state data that had been collected as proof to show the inequitable flow of the money, particularly in the ADAP.

At the annual ADAP Conferences, this information was shared in public meetings, clearly proving that the more urban areas (Part A of the Ryan White CARE Act) were getting approximately twice as much per person as the more rural states (Part B -jurisdictions).

In 1998, Bill Arnold was kind enough to invite me, Kathie Hiers, a relative newcomer to federal HIV policy, to co-host a regional ADAP meeting with him in Birmingham, Alabama. We continued to expose the problematic components of the Ryan White legislation. Being government employees, the AIDS Directors quickly realized that their efforts were hampered to do the advocacy required to get the needed statute changes. The Southern AIDS Directors invited community leaders to join their group, and we held several meetings across the southeast, and changed the name to Southern AIDS Coalition.

In the HIV world, we live in an ever-increasing alphabet soup; everything has an acronym. So, it was an unfortunate realization then that we discovered our groups' moniker turned out to be SADSAC, which simply wouldn't do!

We shortened it to the Southern AIDS Coalition (SAC). The AIDS Directors and the community- based leaders continued to attend bipartisan Congressional meetings and to fight for changes in the statute that would correct the inequitable distribution of the law's funding. Emotions ran high on both sides of the issue.

People who were living in urban areas feared the loss of funding, while advocates in the South begged for enough resources to at least provide life-saving medications. I was often followed at national conferences, such as the U. S. Conference on AIDS, to be heckled and accused of lying. I was shocked to open my emails one morning to find an anonymous death threat! Unfortunately, President George W. Bush was not increasing resources to fight the HIV epidemic domestically.

I remember that at one point in Alabama, more that 1,000 low-income persons living with HIV were on a waiting list to receive medications from the state's ADAP; other southern and rural states were in similar situations. The main principles of the Ryan White CARE act causing the unequal flow of resources were several: those clauses that gave bonus funding to the urban areas; the fact that the bill only counted AIDS cases but no HIV cases, and the law's inclusion counting all deceased persons.

In areas such as the South, which was experiencing a newer epidemic, the ratio of people with HIV diagnoses who had not progressed to AIDS was much greater than in the jurisdictions that had historically had more cases, such as New York and San Francisco. Counting deceased cases was a simple way to continue heavier funding in the areas where the epidemic had begun. Deaths from AIDS were much higher in these bicoastal and urban areas than in the South and rural parts of the country.

After more than eight years of advocacy filled with equal parts vitriol and heartfelt conviction, the Ryan White CARE Act was finally modernized on December 19, 2006. ADAP waiting lists were eliminated and, while still not perfect, the new epicenter of the HIV epidemic received welcome relief.

HEPATITIS AND AGING OF PEOPLE LIVING WITH HIV

Jules Levin, NATAP

With the benefit of drugs and care people with HIV/AIDS live longer but experience unique age-related dilemmas. Jules relates how the system today fails to meet the needs of those with HIV and Hepatitis who are aging. He reports that over half of the 1.2m people with AIDS are over 50, and experience multiple disabilities from "premature aging syndrome." Today, Jules lives with HIV and was co-infected with Hepatitis C for 30 years, but was successfully treated and cured of Hepatitis C. He founded NATAP, the National AIDS Treatment Advocacy Project as a source of state-of-the-art resource and information center.

What we are experiencing now in the era of 21st century HIV are new problems emerging for this first generation of people living with HIV who are aging. Elderly HIV+ are being marginalized because they are not getting their needs met. In retrospect, I can appreciate what the ADAP Working Group and others did to secure care and services plus the accomplishments of the Ryan White CARE Act along with ADAP. But today, we have a unique situation and need something more.

Years ago the ADAP Working Group was a unique model bringing together a collaboration of People Living With HIV (PLWH), industry and advocates, and community-based organizations. At that time, we were fighting for access to the new HIV therapies making them available for all including the poor and uninsured.

Today, however many of those very same people who are 20-25 years older now comprise the first HIV+ elderly community, and many are suffering the "HIV Premature Aging Syndrome." And yet, they have been forgotten. This new problem of premature aging is not getting the attention it needs and is essentially being ignored.

In my early days during the time of the ADAP Working Group I was founder and chief at NATAP (National AIDS Treatment Advocacy Project). I was consumed by HIV care and treatment which at that time in the mid to late 1990s consisted of the 1st generation HIV protease inhibitors and early non-nucleoside reverse transcriptase inhibitors (NNRTIs). Many years later HIV treatment is different and improved with the addition of newer ARTs (antiretroviral therapy) including more effective protease inhibitors, NNRTIs, and integrase inhibitors, along with new combination therapies. We also have new long-acting HIV treatment available for the first time, with additional long-acting drugs, plus new HIV drugs in early development.

But back then, we were all excited and enthusiastic that we had for the first-time new HIV treatments and the political will and administration support to make them available for all. This was the pipeline to save us and provide health and longevity. But the irony now many years later is we have come face to face with a new concern we hadn't even thought of at that time — what happens if you take these drugs and can live a long time? It wasn't even on our radar screen.

So now, aging with HIV has become the elephant in the room. We see life expectancy studies showing reduced lifespan, although much better than before ART. The facts were reported at the most recent study at CROI 2020 (Conference on Retroviruses and Opportunistic Infections) from Kaiser Permanente. This study showed nine years less life expectancy for PLWH who started ARTs with less than 500 CD4s. For all PLWH the study showed that these people experienced early onset of many age-related co-morbidities like diabetes, heart disease, kidney disease, and cancers often 10-20 years earlier than non-HIV people.

Indeed, studies have been reported finding that older, aging HIV+ people experience by five to fifteen years earlier, symptoms of accelerated aging. So now, what we need is a new HIV care infrastructure that meets the needs for our elderly HIV+ population, as well as new reinvigorated research to address the escalating aging/HIV problem.

Today there are 1.2 million people in the US with HIV. Out of this, 280,000 are over 60 years of age and 450,000 are over 55 years. Half of the population with HIV is over 50 and these numbers in each population are increasing every year.

For example, in New York and San Francisco 30-40 percent of people living with HIV are now over 60, and it is estimated that soon 75% of people with HIV in these regions will be over 50 years old. Many older aging HIV+ are suffering; some quite severely, with this premature aging syndrome causing them serious physical and mental impairment or disability, but there is not enough adequate support, care and services to meet their needs. Researchers too, are not conducting the appropriate research to meet their needs.

Due to what I see as gross inaction, I think the federal agencies are simply waiting for us to die. Federal agencies including HRSA (Health Resources and Services Administration), NIAID (National Institute of Allergy and Infectious Diseases), CDC (Centers for Disease Control and Prevention) and HHS (Health and Human Services) just have not yet responded to the problem. They will say they are discussing how to address this issue internally as I speak with them regularly, but nothing has been done about this.

Here in New York City which is the epicenter for aging and HIV and home to 125,000 PLWH I feel the healthcare system is broken, particularly as it affects HIV people. The insurance industry, both public and private, restricts reimbursement to the point that hospitals and clinics are unable to provide the more intensive care required of older PLWH. As well, the community support services are much too inadequate. AIDS service organizations are largely uninformed to specifics of the aging/ elderly HIV+ problems and needs.

It's a real disaster for PLWH who are over 65 with multiple serious health conditions, and as time passes it will become increasingly worse. What goes unappreciated is that the CDC reports 50% with HIV in the USA have detectable HIV viral load, but having detectable viral load significantly increases risk for aging prematurely and contracting co-morbidities.

This is a dire problem and a time bomb waiting to explode. We need a new HIV care infrastructure that meets the needs of the ever- increasing population of our older and aging HIV+ community. HRSA and the RWCA must respond to this problem but so far, they have not.

Unfortunately, HIV policy organizations and advocates are also ignoring this dilemma and except for a very few, there has been no movement towards addressing the needed policy changes that meets the needs of the first elderly PLWHs. The irony of all this is we have been successful in preserving and extending HIV life, only to learn that this longevity brings with it another set of unexpected problems.

AIDS IN MARYLAND -
POLITICS AND DISCRIMINATION

Liza Soloman, Maryland ADAP Director

From an unsympathetic ear to generous funding for AIDS drugs, and cardiac, mental health and Hep C treatments, the state made a complete turnaround. Liza was there at the helm of the ADAP division to witness the transformation.

Originally, I was a public health official with a doctorate in epidemiology and was attached to Johns Hopkins University and researching HIV, injection drug use and exploring how the disease might be spread among drug users. We didn't know how it was being spread and we had an unsympathetic and adversarial Governor who fought a lot of bills.

Then, Governor Parris Glendening was elected and the door to an opportunity for real change with AIDS was now open. His brother had died of AIDS, so he wanted things to be different from now on. Since we were located in the Baltimore-Washington corridor, a dense and highly populated area, it was always 3rd or 4th in the nation with both HIV prevalence and incidence, plus drug use. This is still the case today, but we had access to an area with some of the best medical minds and facilities in that region.

However, it was a different story in rural and remote western counties and the Maryland eastern shore. Luckily, we had enough money to fund clinics and we funded docs from Hopkins to go there. We did the same thing with the rural and remote Cumberland and western region of the state bordering West Virginia.

But one barrier was paperwork; plus transportation was a challenging burden as our policies required clients to come in and fill out a long form every 6 months. We eliminated that by "affirm that nothing had changed" verbally for our eligibility paperwork. Reducing the amount of paperwork, a physician had to fill out helped as well. I remember John Bartlett, MD, the premier HIV researcher saying, "How you are going to live with HIV is directly dependent on where you live." Clients typically had multiple problems even before they got HIV. But in something of a perverse influence, their getting HIV acted as the catalyst that helped them get it together and find a reason to be organized and get help.

And for those patients whose income didn't qualify them for Medicaid but met a certain low-income ceiling they could get pharmacy assistance. Unlike so many other programs we were lucky and had sufficient funds and because of that we had a 50-60 drug formulary. This meant we could offer cardiac, mental health and Hep C treatments since it doesn't do much good if you get your HIV drugs but then you die of a heart attack.

Another thing we did was to create an ADAP-funded insurance program. The reality was some people got great HIV care and not much other care. So, if you could get them health insurance, you could close the gaps, get them full range of services and needed medicines across the board. After 10 years I felt I had done as much as I could, and I think we learned from the HIV effort how important it is that folks most affected were involved in the processes. The entire community helped change how medicine is done to a certain extent. The empowering piece made such a difference to the kind of care we can do.

We should hold onto this for other things as it was a pretty incredible moment and it's hard to fathom where we were, and how far we've come.

MAKING DATA WORK IN MASSACHUSETTS

Philip Olander, Massachusetts ADAP Manager

From independents to chain drug stores, Phil leveraged the benefits of pharmacist reporting along with statistical data collection to manage an evolving new program. His innovations in technology helped keep a steady stream of funding to support and grow his ADAP services.

In its very earliest days, and before there was a Massachusetts AIDS Drug Assistance Program, there was the AZT Reimbursement Program. This was what I call an evolutionary phase when it was pre-Ryan White so there was no secure foundation to keep it going, but it was truly a seat-of-the pants operation in those days. Dorothy Keville recalls visiting me at the office and being astonished that the whole enterprise was being run out of one of my desk drawers, where I had information on 50-60 participants in basic file folders. I remember her saying, "You showed it to me when I visited with you and then I went right over to the Lt. Governor's office to get the left-over money moved to pharmacy instead of letting it go to the general fund!!!"

We were fortunate in Massachusetts that we could find pharmacies willing to participate, however it took some doing to convince them to participate. There was a lot of cold calling to enlist the support we needed. But unlike now, in those days, most of the pharmacies were small, independent businesses rather than chain stores.

The way it worked was, the pharmacies had to mail payment vouchers to me, which I processed by hand for each pharmacy, and there was a ton of paperwork that had to be done manually. At the end of each month, I dreaded having to batch together several weeks of vouchers at a time because if the batch total didn't balance to the penny with the individual vouchers, accounting would reject the whole batch.

Then this meant payments would be delayed. But this attention to detail paid off in a big way one night!

There I was, at my desk working very late one Friday when I got a call from Senator Edward Kennedy's office. They were on the floor of the Senate and wanted to know how much money we needed, and they were calling all the States to get a national budget figure. So, I went through my paperwork data reports, rudimentary as it was, added a contingency and we ended up getting $3M. It was more than we needed but that was how things worked back then before emails.

But by the early 90's the Ryan White Act went into effect and luckily I was in the right place at the right time to bring the program into the modern world. We needed to set up some infrastructure for data collection and by now we had so many applicants that my style of manually operating everything out of a desk drawer was clearly no longer feasible. We outsourced the ADAP program to a community organization and built an infrastructure to collect data for all Ryan White programs.

So now I had a small staff of 2-3 people and together we built a database to collect and organize information on demographics and utilization. It is hard to believe now, but at the time when this started there was no Federal data collection standard for reporting.

By 1992 my team had developed software to collect anonymous demographic and service utilization data. Incredibly, it still took 20 more years for the Federal government to develop a usable software package that actually worked and was reliable. In the meantime, however, in Massachusetts we had amassed a large database of high-quality data for reporting and research purposes.

Because in the early days there was so much stigma and people trying to not make themselves known, it was difficult for them to go to the pharmacy and say that they were participating in the program. It was a challenge for the pharmacies as well. The process for them to get reimbursed was slow and cumbersome, requiring lots of paperwork on their part, and they were being reimbursed only at cost.

While AZT was the first available drug and my office made every effort to get people certified to participate, it was a hard to tolerate drug and turned out to be not very effective by itself. Treatment improved when combination therapy was available. But initially it was a drug of last hope and I remember a lot of sadness with our people, trying to do what we could. It's a different world now.

In Massachusetts we were a lot better off than other places. I am grateful we could help when we could, and I wish more people knew this history.

Public health HIV services are more mainstream and bureaucratic now, but in these early days with HIV, public health was one person at a time, concern for the individuals. Which when you think about it, is really what it should be.

SIDESTEPPING THE RULES - CONDOMS IN CUPBOARDS

Teri Eyster, RN, CM Washington State ADAP Director

The Catholic Church's opposition to use of condoms could have saved lives if it had been supportive early in the pandemic but one clever state Administrator figured out how to circumvent policy that was an impediment. Teri said it was simply a matter of bending the rules and getting everyone to agree that saving lives would be worth it.

It was an amazing time to be in the center of the early days of HIV/AIDS. Now, as I look back on my career that started as a nurse and case manager, I remember how I got involved. My interest in making the transition to HIV was first sparked in 1992 by a sign I saw displayed at the local health department. It read "Be Here for the Cure." For a case manager this is a pretty intriguing invitation, but once I became involved it was a very different arena than I had anticipated.

For one thing it taught me first off that my initial knowledge of boundaries in the medical profession had to be different if we were going to succeed. It took HIV to break down the power dynamic that is so typical between a case manager and a doc and it was an exciting time to see how HIV clipped away at the patriarchy, and how our work was a cross-pollinating collaborative effort across so many teams.

What I think HIV taught people were important lessons that could be applied in a broader scope of health care. For example, caring for people with mental health problems, diabetes, and then they had to step out of their conventional roles to learn how to address their housing needs, manage money and coordinate those funding sources.

We had to do so much more outside the clinic doors. People needed transportation, places to live, and we had to navigate a system that threw us curveballs; we always had to come up with novel means to pay premiums, find medicines and consider out of the box solutions. One scenario in particular was a real benchmark in making a difference. The local health department would not prioritize care services for HIV people and finding help for basic human needs was a messy task, so we decided we would use a not for profit as a contractor to help out.

Our local Catholic Community Services met our criteria as a "compassionate organization" as they had a history of providing free meals and sponsored a once-a-month social event. However, the rule was they could not have condoms on their desk. So, we made a deal with them that once clients came to them, they could retrieve the condoms from a locked closet.

I think too, that as a stage 4 cancer patient my personal experience in HIV/AIDS and helping people with severe illness, loss, grief and stress has helped me cope with my own disease.

We were really good as a group in dealing with HIV clients. We saw death everyday – with our clients, our peers who worked with us – and I think this is why I have been a model cancer survivor. It's a lot worse prognosis than HIV, but what I leaned has literally saved me. I learned how to navigate the local and state services, I learned to not be intimidated by your condition, but moreover I learned strength and beauty in surviving. Now, I call myself terminally optimistic, and I still say today I loved being an ADAP Director, but not a bureaucrat.

BRINGING YOUTH AND FAMILIES INTO THE HIV/AIDS LANDSCAPE

David Harvey, Executive Director, National Coalition of STD Directors;
Founding Director of the National AIDS Alliance for Children, Youth and
Families

When the Federal government was slow to respond to all groups affected by HIV, it took the initiative of private citizens to marshal their energies and resources to get results. Bonding together to create a community who could make a difference always faces uphill obstacles, but David was dismayed at the resistance to include children and families in the HIV/AIDS landscape.

I think it's an accurate observation to say that in its earliest stages, the HIV/AIDS movement was defined by a federal government that took no action. While gay men with HIV were highly visible and had the resources to take to the streets, we knew HIV had already deeply impacted the substance abuse and injectable drug community – the Black and Brown people living in poverty who lacked access to quality health care and education, plus hemophiliacs, and others.

In 1988, I started working on HIV in graduate school focusing on marginalized communities impacted by HIV such as chronically mentally ill adults, homeless people, Black and Brown women, children and families. As an openly gay white man, and as strange as this sounds now, I was openly criticized for abandoning "my own community" impacted by HIV.

I was asked, "Why are you over there working on pediatric AIDS when gay men need you?" In those days, the fault lines were between adults with HIV and kids and tremendous infighting and competition over who got the attention and money.

But I would like to think that I helped to bring the communities together at times, building a cohesive coalition and it was only later that women of color started to get recognition for their very unique needs. When I founded AIDS Alliance for Children, Youth and Families as a national group it had at its heart, the comprehensive, family-centered care and prevention needs of Black and Brown women, their kids and families.

We founded the first Consumer Corps Leadership Program for women of color and its graduates are the women you see today leading our advocacy. But the AIDS Alliance almost did not happen. There was infighting and a drawn-out debate about whether we needed another national group and other factors that almost prevented the organization from coming into reality. And much to my shock and dismay, AIDS Alliance only began after every other national AIDS organization in Washington flatly declared at that time, that kids were not in their mission and they couldn't take us on!

We actually tried to join with other groups but were rejected – that is how deep the animosity ran toward the pediatric AIDS community. It was really an incredible situation. But for me, it was never just about the kids, but it was about the Moms of the kids, their Dads, and their extended family members. We knew HIV didn't just impact kids but on a profound level, the whole family. HIV/AIDS care, research and prevention that met the needs of whole families had to be taken into account – Mom needed help with daycare, transportation, psychosocial support and other care that met the unique needs of families.

I have to say that unfortunately, gay men were not very sympathetic to these needs, at least in the early days. But we turned this around and I am proud of our field accomplishments to serve families impacted by HIV. Nonetheless, there is still a long way to go.

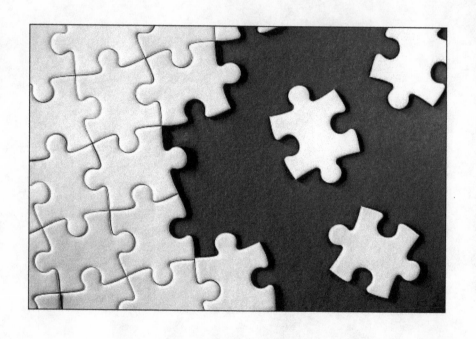

PART TWO

The jigsaw puzzle pieces of every life can often resemble a series of efforts with endeavors tried, some failed, others foiled by circumstance. The puzzle rarely makes sense while living it, and we often ask, who am I? What am I really supposed to do?

When I look back at all the steps of my career, and the role that would never have been obvious at its outset, I realize that yes, there is a subtle, purposeful guidance underpinning each step from people, places, and events that shape us.

We don't often know or can recognize specific turning points until we look back upon them, but one thing we can do is look at our foundation roots to see what lessons we learned, who or what influenced or guided our choices, and what kind of role models and experiences provided our backbone of ethics and resilience.

Here, in Part Two, I go back as far as I remember and as I recall those first years and those years subsequent to early childhood, there is clarity that emerges. I cannot but believe that they surely helped me – to unconsciously choose my path and define my purpose.

CHAPTER ONE
DREAMS AND PARACHUTE BLOUSES

I grew up the oldest of six children in a very strict Irish Catholic family in Lowell, Massachusetts. The nuns who taught at my school made it clear they were instilling a moral compass into their students with one goal in mind: to make the world a better place.

One of my earliest childhood memories is from third grade, gazing out of the window. I was transfixed by fluffy white clouds floating in and out of sight. As my teacher described "infinite possibilities," her words invited me to dream about the woman I would grow up to be. What would I accomplish in life? That day I decided I wanted to be someone who made a difference.

Musing with girlfriends I revealed my dream of "infinite possibilities" as an airline stewardess. I chose Paris, France as my first dreamy destination because I remembered my mother pointing to France on a battered three-foot tall globe in the corner of our living room. Mother reminded me that "our people" had roots in France before they immigrated to their first family home in a town called Trois-Rivieres, Canada and before crossing the border into the US, she told me they wanted to settle permanently among New England Yankees.

In 1948 my parents and my five siblings were known around town as the LeRiche brood. My parents bought our house, a two-story frame structure built in the late 1800s, from relatives for $3,000, which my father described as a "staggering sum."

When our family moved to Lowell, I was excited to enroll in a new school called St. Marie's, the Catholic elementary school. Classes were held in a four-room white frame building. St. Marie's was a full elementary school with eight grades: two to a room.

St. Marie's was organized by the Church to accommodate a large population of French Canadians living in the southern part of Lowell. When I was 10 and supposed to be starting fourth grade, one of the nuns held me back to third grade. She explained that I was transferring from a public school, which was considered inferior by St. Marie's. It was fine with me, it meant I could be in the same class as Barbara, my favorite cousin.

My third-grade class had eleven students in all, three boys and eight girls. In those days, parochial schools were highly regimented and strictly disciplined. Fear trumped learning. At St. Marie's, our morning studies were in French. Afternoon lessons were in English. Most of the families at St. Marie's were bilingual thanks to their Quebecois roots. On my first day, I was overwhelmed when our Sister Superior, regaled in her black robes and white starched cap called my name and beckoned me to the front of the class. I stood filled with shame and tears as she spoke in her native French and I couldn't understand a word.

The nuns became a source of curiosity and adolescent mystery. They were enigmas in their medieval black and white habits, and strict routines of prayer. Another curiosity for me was their unspoken and unquestioning commitment to the teachings of the Church. No one ever questioned what was being taught. As a challenge to their doctrinaire, I imagined asking whether they had hair under their starched wimples, and if so, what color was it? I furtively staked out observation spots as they left our classrooms. Did they ever use the bathroom? Since I never saw them enter our student bathrooms, I decided they most likely never did.

In my ten-year-old mind, the nuns were living deities and not real women. My school uniform was a navy-blue jumper worn over a white silk blouse mother made from parachute material. I wondered how she got a parachute to use for blouse material.

My education continued at St. Marie's with my younger siblings until one of the stricter nuns whacked my cousin with the back of her hand. That prompted our family's exodus via a transfer to the less physically disciplined and more lenient public school in Lowell. I refused to go because, oddly, I felt comfortable at the Catholic elementary school. I was the nun's student helper at the convent – ironing their linens and the Church's linens which were pressed with precision.

My convent work was also an opportunity to continue my part-time career as a nun spy. While I never solved the mystery of their hair color or bathroom habits, I was satisfied being teacher's pet. Looking back, it's apparent they were grooming me to join their order.

But alas, their grooming was all for naught. Although I was at an impressionable young age, I was not interested in a lifetime of deprivation and severe discipline was not the lifestyle I wanted. By my senior year in high school, I was dreaming about finding a husband. He would have the best traits of any man alive and none of my father's most prominent traits.

When I began eighth grade, my mother showed me how she balanced the family budget. As the oldest child, I took her lessons seriously. Every weekend she spread each week's bills on the kitchen table. It was an anxious task as my mother worried that my father's $64 a week salary wouldn't cover the family bills.

My mother wrapped a rubber band around a stack of the money for each bill and sent me off on the bus to pay our debts to stores in downtown Lowell. Usually, one business got short changed. Mother explained that if we paid one dollar that would be enough to convince the store owners, our word was good.

The family's income was tight all year long. One year we kids had to share a gift-a snow sled. It came with all six kids' names on it. On Christmas day we taught our German shepherd, Spike, to put the sled's rope into his mouth and pull us, giving each of us a nice ride around the neighborhood. From my world view growing up, I liked that I had the responsibilities for paying the bills and meeting the business owners who let us put things on lay-a-way. These were some of my happiest memories growing up.

Mother herself was the youngest of six children. Her mother believed she was in high school every day, in reality, she skipped classes to work in one of Lowell's cotton mills with her older sisters. The mills attracted young people from poor homes which meant kids like her lost out on an education. But the money earned from dress mills and shoe shops helped put food on family tables and heat in the stoves.

When she grew up and married, she ran and won a seat on the Lowell Democratic City Committee and wrote letters to President John F. Kennedy. She was invited to his inaugural. I was curious about trying to understand how politics worked. One of my earliest awareness of political protests was when I attended a yearly International Women's Day breakfast at a local college. Our table had a beautiful centerpiece of a freshly baked loaf of bread surrounded by red rose petals. Each table had a card explaining that the bread and roses symbolized a 1912 labor union protest that came to be known as the "Bread and Roses." This strike held in Lawrence, Massachusetts, a town near Lowell was in response to a new state law that reduced the maximum workweek two hours from 56 to 54 hours. Workers were striking against factory owners who responded to the new law by speeding up production and cutting workers' pay.

Women from all ethnic groups banded together in solidarity to shut down their looms, walked out of the mills, and went into the streets to protest. One group of women carried a banner proclaiming, "We want bread and roses too." They wanted fair wages, dignified working conditions, and respect due to them as women, not objects of cheap labor. Their slogan caught on and became the name of one of the most important milestones in American labor history, coming just a few years before women earned the right to vote.

International Women's Day (IWD) commemorated stories of ordinary women who made history often in anonymity. The celebration is rooted in the centuries-old struggle of women to earn equality with men. It's a source of pride that this movement began next to my hometown. Today the Lowell mills are home to artists, museums, and condominiums.

Father was the embodiment of an Irish stereotype. Alcohol was never a stranger. Bill LeRiche was average height, with a commanding presence helped by an ever-present, engaging Irish twinkle in his eyes. He drove a truck to Boston and back to Lowell daily, delivering shoes made in factories around Lowell and Lawrence. He loved to play cards and cribbage with his buddies at the Nickerbocker Club. When he won at the game, we would wake up in the morning to six one-dollar bills on the table. That was a very big deal. Our allowance, if we did all our chores, was five cents a week.

When dad was sober, it was easy to think of him as a loving father. He was kind and a hard worker except on Thursday, payday when he would come home drunk. When he was drunk, he scared me. When the bottle got the best of him, our home was fraught with anxiety for my mother, me, and the whole family. When he lost his temper, we knew he would be violent with my mother. She tried to get him to face his alcoholism, but he denied his problem and was in denial. He tried to make denial work by abstaining from drinking every year during 40 days of lent.

My mother tried to get him to stop drinking. One time she ran out of the house leaving us with him. When she didn't return, it was a living nightmare. He called the police and told them our mother was "missing." The next thing I knew my Aunt Claudia came to live with us. Two weeks later our mother returned after my father agreed to buy me a new bicycle. My younger brother and sisters liked to hang around me all the time, and my mother explained that with a bike, I could go off on my own, finding peace from my dad and my siblings who depended on me. I felt responsible for helping my mother with my younger siblings, but I was learning I needed time alone. This allowed me to daydream about what my future would look like.

In high school, my friends spent hours after school and on weekends debating where they'd go to college. After receiving a one-year offer for a scholarship to Boston University, I had to decline because I couldn't afford the train fare into Boston or money for books.

My dreams of attending college became just that, a dream. After passing the civil service exam I was hired by the Bedford, MA Veterans Administration Hospital working as a medical secretary in the psychiatric admissions ward. I managed admissions for the four psychiatrists in that department. The department head, a psychiatrist interviewing me asked whether I knew how to take shorthand. I replied proudly, "Of course, I learned it in high school." The interview grew uncomfortable. He said, "Well Dorothy, I want you to always remember the first time," and then he pulled me onto his knee and told me to take out my stenographer's notebook and take dictation from him. I didn't know enough to say something about sitting on his lap. I just obeyed. I was only 17 and quite naïve. I was lucky nothing more serious happened. I brushed off the incident because I was happy to earn a $50 per week paycheck. I contributed $30 each week for room and board to my parents.

A few years later, my cousin asked me to be her bridesmaid. At her wedding, I met my future husband. He was the most handsome guy with glasses I had ever seen. He had just graduated from college and the first person I'd ever dated.

I was a bubbly, chatty young woman when we were together while he was always surrounded by his successful college friends. He was quiet and it took me a long time to realize I was starting almost every conversation when we were alone. I worried about the implications of that, but I wanted to be married. It was the societal norm at the time, if you weren't married by the time you were 21, you would surely be an old maid. While I had been attracted to another man at work, after dating Tom for two years, he received a job offer in Elkhart, IN and proposed. I had a proposal to marry and decided I should take it, coming from a big family, I wanted children. I took a job as a teletype operator in Elkhart and within the first year, I was pregnant. My parents drove to Elkhart to see their first grandchild.

I loved being a mother and was afraid I would not know how to care for a baby. Moments of doubt were resolved by having good neighbors across the street I could call on. They adopted two young boys Michael and Patrick and helped me a lot with Kathy. And I loved returning the favor.

When Kathy was just three months old, I discovered I was pregnant and decided I didn't feel comfortable raising my children in Elkhart. There were few things for adults or children to do. We moved to Framingham, MA where I had my second daughter, Karen. I called the two little girls my Irish twins. Who knew back then that one could get pregnant while nursing?

We built a new home in nearby Franklin, MA. for $16,000 in 1961. Right after moving into our new house, my husband was drafted into the Air Force National Guard thanks to the Cuban Missile Crisis. I was expecting our third baby. My husband's paychecks stopped when he was called up, which meant I didn't know when or if I would have money for my children.

I had to learn to drive so I enrolled in a drivers' education course. All I could afford were three lessons. I'll never forget the day of my test; I was in the car's drivers' seat for the first time. Our old car had a single long front seat and when the instructor pulled the seat forward, he made my pregnant belly hit the steering wheel. I yelled, "Ouch!" The poor guy was scared to death and said, "Oh my gosh, I am so sorry, are you ok?" I told him, "Yes, I'll be fine. I'm a little nervous because I have two babies at home and my husband was just drafted into the Air Force. I don't know what I will do if I don't have a license. I am worried if my children get sick, I won't be able to get them to a doctor."

He told me, "Just practice driving in parking lots and you'll be fine," and he put me down as approved for a license. Soon after, I drove our car back home in a blinding snowstorm with two babies asleep in a port-a-crib on the back seat. And I had one more in my belly. I realized at that moment I was on my own until the missile crisis was over. For the first time, I was making major decisions and felt good about the new me.

I remembered my training as a thirteen-year-old when my mother assigned me the task of paying our creditors even when we didn't have all the money. Now I was a mother and once again I was calling creditors that we owed money to, and I had to tell them I'd be late and promise to send a little money each week. I told them they would have to wait until the crisis was over and my husband could get released from the military. On Thanksgiving weekend that year we received word that President Kennedy was sending the troops back home. They were not going to invade Cuba and we avoided a nuclear war with the Soviet Union.

My third daughter, Patti, was born in 1963. Tommy followed two years later and finally, in 1968, my youngest child, Bill was born. I had five children in seven years, and I clearly remember telling myself at that point, "I'm done." This good Catholic girl was exhausted and ready to stop having children.

CHAPTER TWO
PASSAGE TO NEW BEGINNINGS

When my youngest son was six months old, I caught the Asian Flu which developed into walking pneumonia. The doctor called for an ambulance because I was having an allergic reaction to Compazine. My face was paralyzed on one side and my tongue was hanging out. Without my consent the ambulance drivers put a straitjacket on me. I did not need or want it on. I wasn't going crazy, I was having an allergic reaction to that drug, however my husband allowed it. I felt invisible. After a week in the hospital from physical and emotional exhaustion, I was too weak to care for my children, so they went to stay with relatives until I got stronger. This experience and complete lack of control had a tremendous impact making me even more determined to get my strength back and take control of my life.

During my recovery I watched the 1968 Democratic National Convention with interest. It was on television every night while the children slept. Anti-war protesters in the streets outside the convention center were beaten and arrested. I decided that if the Vietnam war wasn't over by the next election, I would get involved. I wanted my voice to be part of the effort to end the war.

In 1971 my husband was awarded a one-year scholarship at Cornell University in New York. He had already been studying at home and received a Master's degree to support his job at the US Army Natick Laboratories. Our family packed up and left for Ithaca, where we rented a house within walking distance of the Cornell campus. I enrolled our two boys at a neighborhood nursery school. I walked them to class every day and picked them up. My girls were enrolled in the local elementary school.

All my children were now in school and I had contacts with several teachers at Cornell. They encouraged me to attend their classes as a not-for-credit student which meant I wouldn't be given a grade, just pass/fail. I was a married woman with five children, and I was enjoying the intellectual conversations as much as learning from the courses I took.

I loved walking to the Cornell campus each day for my audited classes in sociology, psychology, and political science. Even though my grades could not be part of any written transcript, I held my breath each semester waiting to hear if I had passed. That experience made me hunger for the day I could get a real degree.

In addition to attending classes, I set aside one afternoon each week to teach a basic psychology class at my daughter Kathy's elementary school. I worked on a curriculum for the children that engaged them in role-playing. My idea was to introduce them to conceptual ideas like depression, anxiety, and fear.

It was a free-form curriculum that encouraged boys to act in a girl's role, and then other times, and with no advance notice, I asked the girls to adopt the boys' roles. The girls loved it. It was cutting edge at the time in that both sexes shared experiences in gender-identification and how it affected their social relationships.

When my husband finished his year at Cornell in 1972, we drove back to Franklin, MA. on a happy note. I returned to my role as our children's primary caregiver and was feeling physically and emotionally healthy. But at the same time, I knew there was more to life than being a full-time mother.

DISCOVERING POLITICAL WILL

Our move back to Massachusetts from Ithaca turned out to be a catalyst for change in my life.

When we returned, I decided to run as a delegate to the upcoming Democratic National Convention. I supported a strong anti-war candidate, Senator George McGovern. Establishment politicians were supporting Maine Senator, Ed Muskie. I felt empowered to win my campaign as a first-time delegate and was rewarded with a seat at the convention in Miami. I was excited to be making changes with the rest of the political neophytes and radicals who boarded planes for the trip to Miami.

We had a demonstration on the floor of the convention. We each had a letter on our chests spelled out to say, "Stop Dike Bombing." I was the K in Dike holding hands with Abbey Hoffman. Senator McGovern lost the general election in November by a landslide to Richard Nixon. I was so disappointed.

Only Massachusetts and the District of Columbia voted for him. I hoped there were enough other voters in our state and around the country who would vote against the war once they were in the voting booths, but I was wrong. We put bumper stickers on our cars that read, "Don't Blame Me, I'm From Massachusetts."

While the children were still young and going to bed early, I decided to attend school board meetings to listen to adult conversations that were of interest. Then I was asked to chair a school project with other parents to paint our junior high school building along with our children. I chaperoned school trips and was eventually asked to join the town's Finance Committee in Franklin.

I was a total novice and intimidated at first. I had to ask someone to explain how to introduce a budget line item to get transportation funding for senior citizens to go shopping or to their doctors' appointments. One day, I made a motion, thinking that was all I needed to do. I looked around for a second. There was a long pause colored by a stern look from the town's attorney who was also the committee chairman. I held my breath, figuring the hesitation meant the committee would oppose my motion and that would be the end. Finally, after a long silence, one of the older women on the committee seconded the motion and when the votes were added up, I got unanimous approval.

A short time later a friend and I were offered a classroom at Dean College to teach a course aimed at women entitled, Nuts & Bolts of Government: How to Effect Change at the Local, State and National Level. I kept the booklet from our syllabus and still share it with people to this day to help understand the political process. Nuts & Bolts is available under Resources at the end of this book.

It was a weekly course and so many women signed up we encouraged them to bring their children and arranged for a nurse to babysit. Two women in our class ran for local government positions and several of our classmates worked on their campaigns. One woman became Mayor in a nearby town and the other was elected to the Conservation Commission.

Although I didn't have a college degree, I applied for a management position at Wrentham's State School for the Mentally Retarded in 1975. My department hired prisoners from the Norfolk County prison program because the workload kept increasing and I needed help. I taught them typing and general office administration. On one occasion I was called into the prison warden's office about a staff complaint investigation. One of the prisoners filed a complaint against me because I gave his job as our office runner to another inmate. To me, it was a routine decision. But I learned that among our prison workers the runner's job was a source of great competition among the prisoners. I learned a lot about supervising people at that job.

When I saw a staff to client ratio report written by the MA Department of Public Health I saw that we had a huge shortfall in staff for our program, I brought it to Governor Michael Dukakis, knowing full well that the state had a hiring freeze. At our meeting, he wanted to know, "How many staff do you need to ensure our state schools qualify for Medicaid funding?" Then he reminded me, "We can't hire any new people, you know." He was stunned when he saw the staffing shortfall but he approved the 2,800 new staff we needed. That brought in $50 million of federal Medicaid funds into the state coffers, and it got a lot of attention.

In 1976 I was promoted to Director for the Office of Litigation. A Consent Degree at the Federal District Court ordered a wholesale renovation of our state facilities for the mentally retarded. I was hired to oversee the project. I had a corner office working in Boston at the Massachusetts Department of Mental Health, but my marriage was unraveling.

Divorce is a heartbreaking life experience no matter how long ago it occurred. After 17 years of marriage, I filed for divorce, seeking full custody. During the hearing their father wanted full custody as well. I thought that it was in the best interest of my children that they continue living in the family home with their father. I agreed to share joint custody with unlimited visitation rights. The divorce was finalized in 1976. I was 38 with five children ages 9-16. I rented a small apartment halfway between their home and my work. I borrowed a mattress that became my bed and my couch. I experienced negative reactions from people when they heard that my children were not living with me. I faced stigma and discrimination, but it gave me empathy and compassion for others. I continued to work and called my children every night. It was the most painful time of my life but if I was going to get a college degree and get paid a decent salary so they could come live with me, I would need to stop crying and get a degree.

I discovered Antioch University located on Harvard University's campus in Cambridge, MA. Their night classes would allow me to work during the day. I applied and I had documented all my years of volunteer work as well as a recommendation from Governor Dukakis-although I was accepted before his recommendation was sent in. They gave me credit as an equivalent for four years of undergraduate studies and then this qualified me for their two-year Master's program.

I continued to work at the Massachusetts Department of Mental Health and went to school four nights a week and Saturday till 3 PM. I picked up my children after class on Saturday and we spent part of the weekend and school vacations together. I typed my papers on lunch time, drove to Cambridge to attend class and did my readings at night.

After two years, by June of 1978 I had earned my degree (M.Ed.) in Human Social Services Administration from Antioch University.

CHAPTER THREE
PROGRESS AND PERSEVERANCE
IN THE NATION'S CAPITOL

During those next two years while I was taking classes in the evening I remained with the Department of Mental Health and continued to supervise the increased staffing and the renovations of the eight facilities for the mentally retarded, but what I really wanted was a job with the federal government. The work I was doing as Director of the Office of Litigation for Mental Retardation and Mental Health Services was rewarding and personally satisfying but it didn't pay well, and I wanted to work toward a secure retirement and buy a home for my children to come and live with me.

I had heard of a Fellows program in Washington D.C. at the U.S. Department of Health & Human Services (HHS) so I decided to apply. My secretary Maura helped me fill out the forms, but we didn't tell anyone. Maura was living in a rooming house at the time. It was not a great situation and I suggested she come live with me.

The HHS Fellows Program was extremely competitive and a real honor if you were chosen. I was very surprised when I learned my name was on the list of 52 candidates who were chosen from 350 applicants. Each of us were invited to Washington, D.C. for an interview. My 12-year-old son Bill and I took an overnight train into D.C. just to survey the huge government building where I was scheduled to have my interview. When we returned home to Massachusetts, my children and I had a family meeting so I could explain what it could mean for our family.

On the day of the interview, it was pouring rain and when I left the interview, the sun was shining: a good omen. All 52 candidates met separately with a panel that asked us questions. We were told we would be graded on poise, analytical thinking and other factors. We were also told there would be no verbal or nonverbal feedback from the panel, so in other words if you made a good impression, they were not to smile or acknowledge that in any manner.

After I answered all their questions, I was about to get off my chair when one of the women asked me to sit back down. She pointed out that my paperwork did not have the name of my undergraduate school. I responded that when my five children were little, I volunteered for all their activities and that I was involved in many town positions including the Finance Committee and that I was chosen Citizen of the Year. I suggested she look at the back of my application and see activities that I submitted to the University as my substitute for four years of undergraduate work, and that experience had been accepted. I told her I only had a Master's degree. She said with clearly a very verbal enthusiasm, "I think that's great!"

After this interview it was not until the end of May 1980 that I learned my fate. When the official award letter came there were several paragraphs but all I saw was, "Congratulations, you have been chosen as one of 17 Fellows. Please call HHS." Two of the candidates were chosen to work in the Immediate Office of Secretary Patricia Harris. When I called, I was asked to set a date to go to Washington, D.C. for an interview. I told the intern that I only wanted to work in the Boston office of HHS, not D.C. She responded by telling me, "People work for 25 years hoping to get on the 6th floor and YOU don't want to come for an interview?" With that I said, "Yes, I'm happy to come."

Now, it was time to sit down with my children and have the conversation about my move to D.C. I was afraid of what they would think about their mother's new career plans, but as children often do, they surprised me by urging me to go to Washington. They promised they would visit on vacations, and I could fly up to Boston in between, to get my all-important kid fix at least every six weeks. That meant they would remain living with their father. In my absence from them I met four other women who were members of the group Mothers Without Custody. We formed a support group and called it "Offspring" which eventually merged with Mothers. Those cherished relationships with Sue, Bonnie, Maggie and Angie continue today. My secretary Maura decided to make the move to D.C. with me. I was glad for her company and her help with the children when they came to visit.

Despite my reluctance to leave Massachusetts, my children were true to their word. It was a wild and complex juggling act arranging sleeping accomodations, travel, etc., while they were making decisions of their own about jobs or college enrollment. I wanted them to be comfortable with their choices. And they knew I wanted them to come live with me. Eventually, the three youngest moved in with me and Maura after high school and enrolled in local colleges. Their two older sisters enrolled in MA schools. My dream had come true, and my new salary allowed me to buy a three-bedroom, blue stucco townhouse on Capitol Hill in D.C. To help pay for a new roof I joined a Bed and Breakfast association and called our home the Capitol Hill Guest House. With perseverance I was able to pay off the family's school loans.

A SERIOUS CONUNDRUM EMERGES

During this time, I was working long hours at HHS when our office began getting disturbing reports that young men from the San Francisco and New York City area were gravely ill with a form of pneumonia. Most of them were dying. Medically, they presented with very low white blood cell counts indicating a severe immune dysfunction. The Centers for Disease Control (CDC)'s Morbidity & Mortality weekly report for the week of June 5, 1981, recounted the first statistics of what came to be known as the AIDS epidemic.

The CDC, which is part of HHS, assigned 30 Epidemic Intelligence Service officers to a task force to identify the source of the as-yet, unnamed syndrome. In the very beginning, we called it Gay-Related Immune Deficiency (GRID). Bathhouses were discovered to be the prime areas for transmission since gay men with the disease frequented them for sexual liaisons. Cities began to close these bathhouses and epidemiologists were increasingly alarmed as the number of deaths soared, as the disease spread. Officials performed contact tracing to identify the locations and clusters of people with the disease, but it was a different world back then before internet technology and the means to instantly share and convey information.

It wasn't long before we learned the same disease was surfacing in countries all over the world, and Africa was particularly hard hit. Then Asia, South America and the Caribbean . . . it was a full-blown global pandemic. Suddenly, new cases of disease were found in the most unexpected populations. In 1982, infants and adults who had received blood transfusions were becoming ill with the same symptoms as those of the gay men. This presented inarguable and coercive evidence that this was a disease that could be transmitted by blood as well as sexual contact. Nonetheless, it was in the context of sexual contact that became a key factor to drive subsequent events.

The race was on to figure it out. Scientists who transitioned into investigators quickly learned that people with symptoms shared one thing in common: a failing immune system. They had a rare form of pneumonia found in people with weakened immune systems. When their body was attacked by this virus, their ability to fight off the disease was disabled. We were getting reports of other life-threatening opportunistic infections and a malignancy called Kaposi's Sarcoma. The one firm fact we did know was the outcome of a diagnosis of this disease was an irrefutable death sentence, with life expectancy of less than two years.

Once we learned how it was being spread this disease could have been listed as a communicable disease. But those who were diagnosed wanted privacy and shielding from that terminology because insurers refused to provide coverage and businesses refused to hire anyone who tested positive. Further fallout was that people with the disease couldn't get housing. A very vocal activist community grew quickly, and they were enraged at this social injustice, becoming adamant against sharing their disease-related medical information.

One of the divisions in HHS called the Health Resources and Services Administration, (HRSA) took the initiative to begin funding cities hit hardest by AIDS. The population of infected individuals was growing exponentially in major cities affected like New York, San Francisco, Los Angeles, and Miami. But there was no medicine to treat the virus until 1987 when AZT was approved by the Food and Drug Administration (FDA). Unfortunately, even today after all these years, a vaccine has yet to be developed.

During this time President Carter lost his reelection bid to President Ronald Reagan, so my Fellowship was in jeopardy and I was told to get my resume ready and not be surprised if I received a "pink slip" of dismissal sooner, rather than later. Our new President Reagan appointed former Senator Richard Schweiker (R-PA) as the new HHS Secretary. Secretary Harris left – along with all the other Democrats in our office. I, of course, was a known Democrat but when I met Secretary Schweiker, I said to him, "Mr. Secretary you and I have something in common." He knew it wasn't political views. I continued and said, "Well sir, three girls and two boys."

He asked me their ages.

In the end this was an ice-breaker that allowed me to talk him into letting me continue as a Fellow for his Republican HHS department. And I negotiated a two-step salary increase! Now I was responsible for summarizing the weekly issues from our department and charged with sending a two-page summary of information to the President every Friday. But still no treatment for HIV/AIDS.

MY FRIEND MITCH - A VOICE FOR THE HOMELESS

Although President Reagan did not talk about HIV/AIDS in his presidential addresses, he was supportive of helping the homeless, which included people living with AIDS. I had heard of a homeless man named Mitch Snyder who was getting local publicity because he wanted the Reagan Administration to open a homeless shelter in Washington. There were no shelters at that time to house the many homeless who were living on the streets. Mitch was not a typical homeless man, however. A former Wall Street executive, he came to D.C. to live on the steam grates to experience homelessness. He was a member of the Community for Creative Non-violence (CCNV) founded in the early 1970s by Father Guinan, a Chaplain, and participated with a small group of students from Georgetown, forming a grass roots organization protesting the Vietnam War and human rights violations.

To gain sympathy for his cause, Mitch went on a public fast. He refused to eat or drink and was hospitalized in serious condition. Susan Baker, wife of Reagan's Secretary of State James Baker visited Snyder in the hospital, and she knew this was not good public relations for the Administration if allowed to continue. I was assigned to attend weekly meetings in the Baker home to try and find a solution and was asked to write a proposal for the current HHS Secretary's consideration.

As part of the proposal, we wanted to create an Interagency Task Force on Food and Shelter consisting of 13 federal agencies. A meeting was set up with Secretary Heckler and Susan Baker attended with me. At the meeting, Secretary Heckler read the proposal and as we held our breath awaiting her decision, she looked at Susan and said, "I approve it." It was a memorable victory.

As part of the new initiative, 133 food banks nationwide would be able to obtain food at 197 different military commissaries. In addition, 86 cities and towns would be authorized to use empty Federal buildings rent free to house the homeless.

After the meeting, Mrs. Baker went directly to the hospital to tell Mitch that an abandoned Federal building at 425 2ⁿᵈ St, NW suitable for housing 1,000 homeless men and women would be given to him, rent free for one winter. Mitch stopped his fast and he and I negotiated with the D.C government for all the required operating permits. He insisted that only in-kind contributions would be allowed because he knew that if he accepted government money, it may come with unwanted restrictions. The Federal government leased the property to Community for Creative Non-Violence for $1 a year. The phone rang off the hook in my office from people in every state, asking us to remove any red tape that would impede the opening of a local shelter. They also needed access to Federal items such as cots, blankets and supplies in empty Federal buildings. Later the Federal government transferred the CCNV property to D.C.

At the time, many HIV+ homeless clients were unable to obtain medical treatment and Mitch realized he would have to find volunteer physicians to see patients and treat additional homeless-related conditions such as frostbite, malnutrition and mental illness.

Opened in 1983, the first winter came and went. HHS had bins placed in our lobby for winter clothes and our staff were knitting hats, scarfs and gloves. The first Thanksgiving was held in the lobby at HHS. Mitch was supposed to close the shelter in the Spring, but he refused. He went on a campaign pressuring every official he met with. His efforts paid off and in 1984 CCNV hosted a Congressional Hearing in the shelter's basement that eventually led to the enactment of the Stewart B. Kinney Homeless Assistance Act, giving the shelter the authority to remain open.

I volunteered at the shelter every Thursday night and ran a support group for women who had lost custody of their child or children. It was in this setting that I met Deborah who asked me to get her daughter out of foster care. It took several years and many court hearings, but Deborah earned her GED, got a job, an apartment and was allowed to have her daughter stay with her on weekends. I picked her daughter up on Friday and dropped her off on Sunday and wrote reports of their progress for the court.

One night I received a phone call and heard the raspy voice of Mitch. He wanted to know how it was going on the women's side. I have always been grateful that I gave him positive news about Deborah as he had called several of us that fateful night. He committed suicide on July 3, 1990.

But his legacy lives on. The shelter provided many different services including an alternative housing address as one of Mitch's biggest goals was to encourage the homeless to vote. By providing an address he advanced the civil rights of the homeless, allowing them to vote.

When I was introduced to Secretary Heckler I was pleasantly surprised to learn she was from Massachusetts. I was her Public Health Service Manager and I asked to meet with a group that was to develop a teenage pregnancy initiative. The Secretary assigned me to represent her in the White House negotiations. Our policy meetings were convened in the Old Executive Office Building which is considered part of the White House. To facilitate my attendance Secretary Heckler sent her big black car over to pick me up and drop me off each day.

I listened and was careful to give the Secretary's input without divulging her position. At the end of each meeting, I went back to my office and wrote a report. The day finally arrived when members of Reagan's Cabinet scheduled a vote. My task in all this was to assemble packets of information known as Decision Memos, that would be distributed to each Cabinet Secretary. I got a notification that the cabinet was meeting at an earlier time and Secretary Heckler needed the packets delivered immediately. With the help of other staff members, we quickly created additional packets. Since the Secretary had laryngitis, she instructed me to attend the meeting in case she could not speak, warning me I might have to be her voice. Her big black car drove me through the White House gate, and I was escorted up the winding staircase into the White House Cabinet Room with all men sitting at the table. The Secretary and I were the only women in the room.

I was nervous but since I wrote the proposed policy position, I realized I could make the presentation if the Secretary needed me to. It was the first time in my life that I felt total peace and confidence in knowing that I was a strong, capable woman able to handle a major national public policy issue; taking it from a proposed piece of legislation to getting input from knowledgeable experts, and finally, seeing it through to implementation into law or being rejected outright.

Secretary Heckler had indicated prior to our meeting that she wasn't sure if she had enough votes to defeat the proposal as it would be detrimental to young women of color. She got her voice back and was able to do the presentation which persuaded enough Cabinet Secretaries to kill the initiative. I felt privileged to be present for the debate since no Democrat would have knowingly been invited into a Republican meeting and at the end of it all, we rode back to HHS together in the Secretary's big black car, satisfied we had gotten the job done as she had intended.

At the time I thoroughly enjoyed working on public policy issues for HHS but began to feel the nudge for a new adventure, preferably with a salary increase.

By the time I was working for Secretary Heckler I was already doing the work of a GS-15 staffer who was paid about $68,000 a year in 1984, even though I was officially a GS-14, which was 10,000 less.

Word had gotten around about my experience and I was offered a GS-15 position in what is now Centers for Medicare & Medicaid Services (CMS). But I needed to first send my request to take this position to Secretary Heckler who would need to approve the transfer. Her Chief of Staff came to my office threatening to block my move saying the Secretary wanted me to stay, and she would not approve my promotion. While I had a large, beautifully furnished office with a view of the Capitol, this was not good news, and I foresaw my future stagnating without what I considered proper compensation. The prospect of leaving the Federal government was something I had to really consider seriously.

To think about it, I took a week off. My daughter Patti and I drove to Cape Cod, took long walks on the beach and talked about my future and whether I should resign HHS for a new opportunity that was opening at the American Pharmacist's Association (APhA), which conveniently was also in the heart of Washington. On my last day, Secretary Heckler called me into her office, thanked me for all the work I did for the Public Health Service over the last four years at HHS, and gave me her blessing along with an award in recognition of my service. It was the end of an era and I was on to new things: always exhilarating but a bit frightening.

CHAPTER FOUR
PHARMACISTS LINCHPIN
TO LIFE FOR HIV/AIDS

While I was at HHS a pharmacist friend told me that the American Pharmacists Association (APhA) was hiring a new President. A new executive often means new staff. My friend thought I would be perfect, and she scheduled a meeting. After that I got the job. It was an incredible opportunity to be hired by this national organization as their first Director of Government Affairs, representing 40,000 member pharmacists. One of my initiatives was to contact the 50 separate state pharmacy associations and bring them under the umbrella of APhA. I brought pharmacists to receptions held by Congressional members in their home districts. This way, the pharmacists could meet with their elected representatives who were voting on issues that concerned them directly.

We published a handbook that helped the pharmacists understand the organization's issues and their importance. We featured a picture of our stunning APhA building on the cover. I saw it was crucial to develop policy positions that would help put us in front of legislators since up until my arrival, Congress did not have any contact with APhA and its member concerns. Prior to my appointment, they had been content to be a sleepy non-profit, operating under the naive premise that they should wait for Congress to call them when they were needed, instead of the other way round. But I saw my role differently and the booklet was key in clearly outlining all APhA policy positions. We delivered the booklets to all Members of Congress.

Then I registered as their Federal lobbyist and started a Political

Action Committee (PAC). It didn't take long for the White House to take notice and soon we were invited to Congressional receptions. We were also invited to attend events at the White House and to testify before Congress.

One very interesting project was lobbying Congress to support drug diversion legislation which was designed to discourage drugs from being channeled to illegal markets. I partnered with the staff of Congressman John Dingell (D-MI) to draft drug diversion legislation to discourage drug samples from being kept in the trunk of pharmaceutical sales representatives' cars. The problem was not just the storage, but the effect on the product in heat and humidity, in hot and cold weather sometimes for long periods that would destroy the efficacy of the drug. At the time, there was no tracking mechanism to account for what happened to the samples. Our bill required pharmaceutical salespeople to track the samples they carried around with them.

Of course, this proposed legislation attracted opposition from 18 pharmaceutical companies who instructed their lobbyists to defeat the bill. During the Congressional hearing when the APhA president was testifying before the public and Members of Congress I brought a cameraman to film the proceedings. My idea was that this footage would be used later as a teaching tool for our members to learn how to effectively present an issue, and pressure their Members of Congress to support the bill.

On the day Congress voted on the diversion bill I went to the Pharmaceutical Research & Manufacturers Association (PhRMA) offices so I could watch the vote on television, since we didn't have a TV at APhA. The other drug company lobbyists were already celebrating, telling me they were convinced our bill would not pass.

I was there when the 18 big Pharma lobbyists sat around the table watching the debate and each of us threw a dollar bill on the table. They told me, "Dorothy, you're going to lose!" They started picking numbers for the spread. They thought they were going to win. I said, "Yeah sure. I'll take the biggest spread because I plan to win." When the vote was taken and our bill passed, I picked up the $19 and walked out.

After that, the pharmaceutical industry association took notice of my effective tactics and I began getting recruitment inquiries from large companies. It was an intriguing and lucrative opportunity so I talked with friends who were pharmacists, asking which of the companies I should consider working for. They recommended Burroughs Wellcome, a hundred year-old company originally founded in England and named after two pharmacists, now with U.S. headquarters in North Carolina. The company was making headlines because they had just announced a breakthrough drug called AZT that had been FDA-approved for the treatment of HIV/AIDS.

Burroughs Wellcome's AZT approval in 1987 got everyone in the AIDS community's attention. This approval, however, was six years after AIDS was identified in 1981 and it would not be until 1994 when the more effective, and less harsh combination antivirals were approved. When AZT was announced there was widespread hope that finally there was a company with a drug to help those with AIDS. However, a big obstacle was the asking price of up to $10,000 a year and Burroughs Wellcome was the only company manufacturing AZT.

At the time, I viewed AIDS as the biggest public health problem in the world, decimating lives indiscriminately. I remembered my days at HHS when we first heard about HIV and working for this company appealed to me. But like many other remarkable innovations, the development of the drug has an interesting backstory.

AZT was first developed by Jerome Horowitz in 1964 and it was initially designed as cancer chemotherapy, but it wasn't effective for that purpose. It was Drs. Francois Barre-Sinoussei and Luc Montagnier and colleagues from the French Pasteur Institute who described the causative retrovirus in 1983. Then in 1984 Dr. Robert Gallo and his colleagues at the National Cancer Institute at NIH demonstrated additional proof of causality and in their laboratory found sustained viral growth of that retrovirus in vitro.

The product that had been mothballed years ago was resurrected and found to be effective against HIV, and it was this chain of events that launched its development as an AIDS drug. When the CDC hosted the First International Conference on AIDS in 1985 it was attended by over 2000 registrants seeking more news. In 2008, the French researchers Barre-Sinoussei and Montagnier were awarded the Nobel Prize in Medicine for their discovery of Human Immunodeficiency Virus (HIV).

I was really motivated to work on HIV/AIDS so I approached Burroughs Wellcome and proposed they hire me. It was a successful if not somewhat bold move and in 1987, they assigned me to the position of Regional Government Affairs Manager with responsibility for 14 East Coast states. I opened a Federal office for the company on K St. in Washington, D.C.

Somehow, I already knew that every ounce of prior work, advocacy and career achievement under my belt would play a part in what was to come with this company. I foresaw that my efforts could be an instrument to advance important change in combating the AIDS pandemic.

One day, while in my Washington lobbyist's office, I saw a pink telephone slip on my desk. The message was from Buddy Clark. He was my neighbor on Capitol Hill and he was inviting me to the Human Rights Campaign annual dinner and asked if I wasn't planning on wearing my blue sequin dress, could he wear it. He was on our Burroughs-Wellcome Community Advisory Board as well as our Patient Assistance Program. At the time he was the longest living person in our clinical trial using AZT who had HIV/AIDS.

Buddy was born in Atlanta and had moved to D.C. He had both a lovely southern drawl and a wonderful sense of humor. He'd say, "Girl, if I wasn't gay, I'd be chasing your skirts." Buddy also performed impersonations of Carol Channing singing Hello Dolly at gay events. He was very funny and loved to make everyone laugh.

When Buddy was dying of AIDS Wasting, the ravages of the end stage of this horrible disease, I arrived at the hospital to see him. I was told "Immediate relatives only," but I told the nurse I will only stay a few minutes so I can say goodbye. I went to his room. His family had not yet arrived, and Buddy was shivering in his bed despite wearing a bathrobe and covered in blankets. I smiled at him and crawled into his bed, holding him to warm him and began to hum lullabies. Through all this, nurses came in and out, checking his vital signs. When his family arrived, I got out of bed and held his hand to say goodbye.

Buddy never showed the public face of how HIV had affected him emotionally. Even his last words to me had a tenderly comic overtone, "Don't let anyone ever say that we didn't sleep together. I shed many tears over losing Buddy and countless others who died of this horrible disease."

CHAPTER FIVE

ANECDOTES ON ACTIVISTS, AIDS AND ADAP — ENDLESS ROUNDS OF LEGISLATIVE CHALLENGES

As we fast approached a new decade, the 1990's, part of my responsibilities with government affairs was to attend health care hearings held by state legislatures. These meetings were designed to address issues that policymakers had concerning any pharmaceutical products manufactured by Burroughs Wellcome. The meetings were open to the public and AIDS activists often attended, particularly to protest the high cost of the drug AZT.

For example, in Massachusetts, the activists proposed a Trade Secret bill that would require Burroughs Wellcome to release details on how the drug is made. However, this was proprietary information and could not be made public, so their effort was unsuccessful.

After months of negotiation with activists, legislators, agencies and others, I baked dozens of white chocolate chip cookies to bring to what turned out to be our final meeting. The protesters knew our position wouldn't change but I felt I had to somehow make an effort that would go toward building trust. Sometimes sharing food, in this case cookies, can say more than words. We were able to agree to disagree. I also brought a black and white framed print of Robert Mapplethorpe's photograph of an arm — it was a gift for the most vocal activist. It was my way of acknowledging his strength and determination. Mapplethorpe died of AIDS and is buried in Massachusetts.

In another scenario there was a Massachusetts bill on Off-Label Use of Prescription Drugs for Breast Cancer that Senator Nancy Sullivan (R-MA) asked my help to get passed. We were both from Lowell and she was scheduled for her second mastectomy with plans to retire. She wanted one last piece of legislation before she gave up her seat. However, it was not a Burroughs Wellcome drug that would be affected in this proposed bill.

Off-Label then and now, means that when an approved drug is prescribed to treat one disease, and there is evidence that drug might help treat another disease, physicians are legally allowed to prescribe it. However, insurance companies typically refuse to reimburse the cost by saying it is "experimental." Senator Sullivan wanted insurance companies to be required to reimburse for treatment. So given her situation I agreed to help and partnered with another industry lobbyist, Bruce Engle from Lederle Labortories to pass a bill that would require insurance companies to pay for Off-Label drug use for breast cancer.

Hearing this, the AIDS activists went to Burroughs Wellcome and complained that I was trying to oppose language they wanted expanded in the bill. They felt this bill should include paying for Off-Label use of medicine for AIDS and since it did not, they were opposed to the bill's passage.

The activists asked for a meeting with decision makers at Burroughs Wellcome. We were in that meeting discussing this issue along with other topics when the activists voiced their complaint about me and the Off-Label bill. I passed a note to my boss who passed it to the President explaining the situation because it was embarrassing that he did not know all the facts and it certainly positioned me unfavorably.

I said this bill was for Off-Label breast cancer only drugs, but I had earlier reassured the activists that in the next year I would work to get Off-label AIDS drugs included. And in fact, I was successful and in the coming year I got the bill amended for Off-Label AIDS drug use passed.

On the night of the vote it was the last legislative session of the year and we found out someone was changing the language, but we were able to get a Senator to remove that language. Then a House member 'pocketed' the bill and went to dinner. They don't actually put it in their pocket, but they might as well have. What that means is they literally stall the vote hoping that the deadline for voting will pass and the bill could not be considered so in effect it fails. While we were stunned, we asked the Senator who we could call to intervene.

What she did was very bold but effective. She called the editor of the Lowell, Massachusetts Sun to ask for help. The editor then left a very specific message for the House Representative who was calmly eating dinner assured he had killed our efforts. In short, the editor said that if he didn't let that bill get voted on, every time a woman dies of breast cancer, we will put that in the Lowell Sun and blame you!

The outcome was that the member released the bill for consideration, and after running back and forth between the House and the Senate, it passed. Despite the number of votes for approval, you're still not done. The final step is it must be typed on parchment paper in the document room before being given to the Senate President for signature!. No one was allowed in the document room, but another woman Representative barged in screaming our bill number until they threw her out.

The clock was ticking, and it was now 11:45 pm, midnight was upon us; by the time it was typed it was 30 seconds before midnight. Making it under the deadline was never more appropriate than that night and it was the most difficult piece of legislation that we had ever lobbied. With that initial piece under our belts, we were able to work with the activists in Connecticut, Rhode Island and New York to get similar legislation passed the following year and to include amendments for AIDS drugs.

Burroughs Wellcome was called to answer charges of price gouging at a hearing scheduled in NYC. I was advised by our legal counsel not to show up. There was an empty chair for me with a spotlight on it. However, while I was absent from that event, I was later able to meet with an NYC Assemblyman's staffer to explain why the drug cost so much. I explained that in the beginning, the active ingredient in AZT came from herring and salmon sperm extract, which required 15 different processing steps to manufacture and live marine resources in the hundreds of millions just to extract the essential component. This was an incredibly expensive undertaking and justified the production cost. Of course, at the time, no one knew any of this and in fact, Burroughs went so far as to employ a man with a shotgun stationed on the production line to prevent theft. I saw the man myself. The processing included having to build a fire station. This was just part of the landscape in this new activist versus corporate environment that clashed over access to life-saving medicines. A lottery had to be set up for distribution of AZT since the supply was limited in the early days.

It is an understatement to say that relationships were adversarial between drug companies and activist groups such as ACT-UP. The legislators also complained about the cost of AZT. Protests over this cost were routine and usually became angry; even violent. There was one unforgettable occasion when a group of activists climbed up on the roof of one of our plants in North Carolina to pour fake blood over the sides of the building. That event caused $9,000 worth of damage and subsequently the company had to hire guards to protect its plants and staff. During our meetings activists would chain themselves to desks to call attention to the price of AZT. Another grim event occurred when the activist group ACT-UP halted traffic on Wall Street by carrying empty coffins through the streets. Every day there was a new media headline of one sort or another all focusing on the condemnation of the drug price, and the number of people dying from this disease.

In 1991 the Health Resources and Administration (HRSA), which is part of HHS, was given an appropriation of $30M to provide eligible individuals therapeutics to treat their HIV or the care and treatment needed to prevent the serious deterioration of their health. This included measures for treatment of opportunistic infections but while the funding continued it was not nearly enough. People were still dying.

In the fall of 1994, I was called to a meeting in Albany to represent Burroughs Wellcome where groups of activists were loudly protesting drug prices. They demanded to know why drug companies didn't lower prices and why Burroughs wasn't offering grants to support AIDS patient care. This was the atmosphere typical of our meetings with activists: they were complaining about the cost of AIDS medicines across the table to the pharmaceutical companies who were selling those same medicines for a profit. A conflict of people and profits is the argument I heard dozens of times, but it remained an unsolved stalemate of enormous proportions. We needed a fresh start.

CHAPTER SIX
AN OLIVE BRANCH
ON BOTH SIDES OF THE TABLE

It was December of 1994 and time for a new strategy. I suggested a series of meetings between opposing groups but with new ground rules. I reminded the rowdy activists that with me as a liaison, they had the opportunity to get the ear of the entire drug industry. But I had conditions and I told them that if I set up meetings at Burroughs Wellcome's D.C. office conference room, could I trust them to act professionally or did I need to rent a conference room in a hotel? Would they behave and not try to handcuff me to my chair or disrupt the meeting in other ways? They agreed to my rules of behavior. With their assurance I then invited 18 AIDS activists to the meeting along with the industry representatives. It would be an even number:18 activists and 18 companies from industry.

At the first meeting held in the Burroughs Washington office, representatives from the 18 major pharmaceutical companies sat in the back of the room and were asked to listen but not speak. I wanted representatives for the 18 activist groups to air their grievances uninterrupted. This was very nerve-wracking because I didn't know if anyone would show up or how they would behave at the meeting. It was with great relief and a pleasant surprise when the activists arrived wearing suits. And, they had left their signature handcuffs usually attached to their belts, at home.

Nonetheless it was a tense room. The drug companies did not trust the activists and the feeling was mutual. I had lunch delivered because I knew many activists were HIV+ and needed to take their medicines with food every four hours. Once again, the activists started the dialogue with demands for reduction in the cost of the HIV/AIDS drugs and I knew the industry representatives were having hard time listening to their angry outbursts. However it was in everyone's best interest to hear them out.

After several meetings, the activists asked companies to make a public statement in support of the Ryan White CARE Act which had already passed Congress with an appropriation of $30M for Fiscal year 1990. That money was earmarked towards states' purchases of AIDS drugs under Title II of the CARE Act. Up to now, the industry had not taken a position on reauthorization of the CARE Act which would be important for the next go-round appropriation of funding.

Working together in this fashion, our ad hoc committee of activists and industry eventually became known as the AIDS Drug Assistance Program (ADAP) Working Group whose focus was getting a $52M appropriation for Fiscal Year 1995. For purposes of brevity, we shortened it to the ADAP Working Group.

Over the next several weeks, all 18 pharmaceutical companies agreed to the language in the CARE Act, but one of the activist stipulations was that it had to be put in writing for an upcoming Congressional hearing that was scheduled in the next few days.

I asked Rich Tafel, an AIDS activist with the Log Cabin Republicans, to help me write the hearing testimony. The Log Cabin Republicans is a national organization of lesbian and gay Republicans with 43 chapters in 32 states. At the time, Rich was a member of our Working Group and was responsible for the increase in funds that exceeded President Clinton's budget request. Rich also worked with Representative Tom Coburn, MD (R-OK) who supported the budget increase, and he went to the House floor to make the request.

Meanwhile members of the Working Group made appointments with all the committees to give them the data on why we needed approval for additional funding. When these meetings were set up with the policymakers there was to be an activist and an industry person at each one. This was a great strategy and it worked. Industry could not ask for funds that would help their bottom line, and legislators were not setting up any meetings with activists they did not know; they did not want people chaining themselves to furniture in their offices.

Through his connections Tafel met with the Republican Members who sought more AIDS funding than the Democrats. Representative Coburn's staff were very helpful in persuading their boss to sign a joint letter with Representative Nancy Pelosi asking for additional ADAP appropriations.

We worked until 2 a.m. drafting the statement from industry which I faxed it to all 18 pharmaceutical companies saying this is what was going to be used in the hearing based on already agreed upon facts. No emails at that time!

Working together we achieved a significant victory by streamlining the new drug approval process through the FDA. This was a fantastically welcome FDA reform of major proportions. That reform, along with designating the AIDS Drug Assistance Program (ADAP) as the "buyer of medicines" became the springboard for developing and approving the cascade of new AIDS drugs quickly coming to market.

This written testimony we created was also important for winning Congressional reauthorization of the Ryan White CARE Act. We got the industry statement submitted on the record at Senators Ted Kennedy and Nancy Kassenbaum's hearing two days later, February 17, 1995.

Despite all our efforts, Congress did not appropriate any funds for FY'95. By that fall, the appropriation process began but there was no line item earmarked for states to pay for AIDS drugs.

However, we felt we had an ace in our pocket: evidence. To help convince legislators to pass an appropriation, and provide the funds needed, Bill Arnold, an activist who had founded the Community Access National Network, partnered with NASTAD to gather expenditure evidence on HIV/AIDS medication. Then along with an industry representative we took that documentation and went together to meet with Members of Congress.

We had compelling data on how many people in their respective states/district had AIDS and how they would be affected by not having the drugs they needed. If Congress refused people access to the medicine, they needed it would not reflect well on them. At the meeting, we tried to get the Members to commit their support to fund the financial assistance needed in the form of an appropriation. Upon leaving the meetings, we tallied our results and reported the good news back to the committee. Our efforts were successful, and we received full funding of $52M for States to purchase drugs for HIV/AIDS. Pharmacists were now able to stock more drugs. Our strategy worked!

YEARLY ADAP BUDGET - FUTURE FINANCING

The ADAP program is officially designated as a "discretionary program," which means that spending isn't an automatic handout from the government each year, but it is subject to appropriations. In other words, the money needs to be decided upon each year, or however often the law stipulates by the Congressional budget process. As is often the case, what you need and what you get can be very different.

One of our requests to Congress was that they pay for drugs for half a year, as this would assure people that their ADAP source of medicine would be secure for at least six months. Congress authorized $10M, which meant they essentially approved this amount, but only appropriated funds at half that level, $5M. So now, with only half of what we needed to fund medicines for AIDS patients at the peak of the AIDS pandemic, it looked like our program was going to end.

At the same time, there was a corporate take-over in process and Burroughs Wellcome was about to be bought out. Recognizing I had a slim window of opportunity before the takeover I made what might be the most daring and ultimately successful effort to help the AIDS community in their funding dilemma. If we didn't get the additional $5M, patients would not be able to get their medications. They could die. I remember sitting in my office and praying for an answer. We could not get more funding out of Congress. What could I do? I pleaded with my boss to give $5M directly to HHS, telling him this was what we needed to make up that year's budget shortfall. He agreed with certain very firm conditions; there was to be no publicity, no fanfare.

There are really no words to describe the elation of going to North Carolina to personally pick up a $5M check knowing that the piece of paper in my briefcase would make a difference to countless people with AIDS.

Upon my return to Washington, I told the Working Group about the contribution, but make it very clear that there could not be any announcement. Then I made an appointment with HHS to hand deliver the check. It was a very unusual situation and possibly a first: industry helps out the government with a private contribution of funding. When I arrived at HHS, I visited my old office and some of the policy managers I had worked with but did not tell them I had a check for $5M in my briefcase. When I met with then Secretary Shalala to hand over the check it was unreal as no publicity or fanfare was allowed. When I left the building, I had a moment of private jubilation knowing I had been the one to orchestrate and incredible feat!

By June 1995, the corporate changeover had taken place and Burroughs Wellcome was bought out by GlaxoSmithKline, another company located in Research Triangle Park, North Carolina.

Although the new owners asked me to consider going to work for Glaxo, I took the separation/retirement package offered and moved back to Massachusetts. It was time to put all I had learned and accomplished to work for myself, and my reputation was well known among all sectors of the AIDS arena. I began consulting with Merck Pharmaceuticals and other drug companies who were manufacturing AIDS drugs. Merck also agreed to keep paying my expenses so I could continue representing the pharmaceutical industry on the ADAP Working Group.

In my role as consultant and co-chair on the Working Group representing industry, my colleague and co-chair Bill Arnold, represented the AIDS community activists. Together we made a good collegial team. Another activist who was also an attorney, Gary Rose, helped set up four committees within our organization: a legislative, budget, data and public relations committee. We met monthly in Washington with the entire ADAP Working Group for the sole purpose of getting funding for people living with AIDS. No other issues could detract from our mission. For a fee, other industry members could join us and attend all our meetings. One of our biggest draws were our conferences that brought speakers to address and update us on different issues; which was a huge benefit to State AIDS Directors who came to hear the latest news, progress and concerns.

It was important for our ADAP Working Group to stay connected with things happening in other parts of the world. This was not a disease confined to our borders as issues were universal in nature. Since HIV/AIDS was a global pandemic and there were annual International AIDS Meetings, I went to industry asking to fund our group's attendance at all them. I was privileged to attend two meetings, one in Vancouver and one in Geneva. Members of our Working Group presented 'posters,' informal gatherings on the convention floor to present a specific issue.

I'll never forget the Geneva event. Our sponsor's table was paid for by an industry representative and I expected to be given enough tickets at the big dinner to distribute to the guests. Someone deliberately gave my tickets away, so when I arrived at that table, I saw that all nine seats were occupied by gay men. I tried to take a seat and was unceremoniously told it was reserved for a man. Then, Bill Arnold, my ADAP co-chair who was sitting among them, said, "Dorothy, I want you to sit down."

I knew that being a heterosexual woman working with gay men might not be easy, and this occasion was not the first time gay men made me feel unwelcome. The irony of the situation was apparently irrelevant. The very seats they occupied were funded by the pharmaceutical companies of which I was the representative, and it was directly through my efforts that activists and industry were brought together to help them.

When we started the ADAP Working Group we had routine presentations by the Kaiser Family Foundation who presented the data they were collecting on HIV/AIDS throughout the country. We used the Kaiser information along with data collected by the National Association of State & Territorial AIDS Directors (NASTAD) as the evidence to convince Members of Congress to fund the AIDS medication and care programs. We had 'sign on letters' by a Member of the House and Senate with signatures by as many Members as we could gather in support or as a co-sponsor of an appropriation each year. Then in 1997 we sent a letter to all the Governors asking them to add state funds to pay for AIDS treatments. This strategy proved to be very successful as the governors responded positively. Our efforts, along with advocates and activists were well received and Congress has continued to fund Title II of the CARE Act to the present day.

CHAPTER SEVEN

FOCUS ON A VILLAGE SPRINGBOARD
TO THE WORLD AND BACK HOME

Since our lobbying effort on AIDS Federal funding had reached a level of $900.3M and was continuing at that level of appropriation each year, I decided it was time for a new direction. After five years I stepped down from the Working Group as Co-Chair and Bill Arnold continued as Chair. I felt a calling to put my efforts toward international AIDS. When I announced my retirement from the Working Group in 2000, I received a lovely Tiffany crystal bowl from Sandra Thurman, the Clinton AIDS czar given in recognition of my contributions. It is still a prized possession.

During my career as an industry consultant, I met Barry Childs who had been affiliated with Abbott Labs. He had aspirations to start a not-for-profit organization transforming the lives of vulnerable children in Tanzania. After leaving the world of ADAP I felt I could put my energies toward helping Barry realize his philanthropic vision of bridging the East and the West. The Bridge was to be the representation of connections of ideas, funds and commitment to help children in Tanzania.

Barry formulated the mission of Africa Bridge to transform the lives of children, an East African country hard hit by the disease with few resources. I suggested we contact the 1983 Nobel Peace Prize winner Archbishop Desmond Tutu who had just released a book "No Future Without Forgiveness," to ask if he might somehow endorse our mission. Barry asked Abbott Labs to pay for our travel to Toronto, Canada where the Archbishop was on a tour promoting his book. However, as I went through customs, the border guards asked for my passport. I told them, "I forgot it, but you have to let me come into Canada because I have a meeting at 3 p.m. with Archbishop Desmond Tutu!" To my great surprise, the Royal Mounties let me in, and we were able to attend the Archbishop's speech on his newly launched book.

After hearing the Archbishop speak, I was convinced more than ever that we had to have him on our Board of Directors. We approached him after his address and introduced ourselves and our idea. He told me, "I don't join any Boards." However, I was wearing my Benedictine Oblate religious medal for the occasion and I boldly countered with, "Archbishop, we came all this way to invite you to join our Board of Directors for the creation of an Africa Bridge that will bring East and West together. We want to help orphans whose parents have died of AIDS in Tanzania." I was shameless as I kept touching my medal while talking to him because I knew he would surely notice that. Then we had pictures taken with the Archbishop during which I smiled while silently saying a prayer. Afterwards, he relented and said, "Alright, yes, you can use my name." Having the name of this global figure whose reputation was of the highest caliber on our initial Board not only helped us raise funds it also made it easier to recruit celebrities and corporations as donors.

After its initial founding, Barry Childs set up Africa Bridge as a non-profit organization with on the ground efforts concentrated in a village located in the southeast portion of Tanzania.

"We set up our program with income- generating cooperatives for families who are caring for HIV/AIDS orphaned children. These co-ops have now trained over 300 Tanzanian volunteers to provide psychosocial and other services to vulnerable children and their caregivers. Africa Bridge has a proven track record of dramatically increasing incomes for our participating Tanzanian caregivers. So now, along with our financial support, they can send their children to school, give them three meals a day, and provide basic health care. Most caregivers in our co-ops are women whose involvement has given them an avenue to new opportunities. By implementing cooperatives we have enabled them to not only provide services to the children in their communities but also provides the means for them to start businesses, participate in their local government, and raise standard of living.

Here's how that all works. In exchange for microloans provided by Africa Bridge, the caregivers agree to house a child and send them to school. The cost is $25 per child. That sum covers food, housing, education, school uniforms, shoes, and writing materials for the entire year. Under this plan some caregivers – mostly women – were able to buy small livestock and created chicken and pig farms. When they pay off their loans, they can invest their profits in other businesses. I'm happy to report that our first female entrepreneur now has five businesses. Clearly, it is a scheme that works to the good of all involved.

We held a wonderful fundraiser in Portland, Oregon that raised $30,000 for Africa Bridge and that alone enabled us to open five more co-ops at a cost of $6,000 each. Then we also began another stand-alone program in Tanzania to teach life skills to adults who can then teach their children how to make better decisions for themselves, including how to stay healthy.

Our co-ops are filled with people who are hopeful and motivated, who have basic life needs met and who can grow and thrive in a positive environment. Children and adults together make life better for their entire communities. Our Africa Bridge model has been replicated in 37 Tanzanian villages and we are currently touching the lives of approximately 10,000 vulnerable children."

In 2010 Barry was awarded the AARP Purpose Prize. Called You live. You learn. You give back. This award celebrates people 50 and older who are using their life experience to make a difference.

After helping launch the Africa Bridge initiative my interest was still focused on HIV/AIDS treatments. I had heard alarming reports that the Health Minister in South Africa was allowing AIDS treatments dispensed that were not approved or scientifically proven to be effective. To learn more about this situation and find out what exactly AIDS patients in South Africa were being given I traveled to Johannesburg. Then, as a guest of the Themba Lethu Clinic, which is the HIV Research Unit associated with Chris Hani Baragwanath, the largest hospital in South Africa, I made an appointment to meet with the Medical Director. She walked me through their patient intake area, explaining that was where new patients asked questions and got answers and also where patients are examined and tested for HIV. If they're found to be infected and need drugs, they are given three month's supply. Then, when I asked to see what drugs they were giving, she took me into a part of the clinic secured by three locked doors and showed me the same combination therapy drugs we were using in the US.

The Medical Director told me a story about an older woman who came into the clinic in a wheelchair. She appeared to be dying of AIDS, but she kept insisting that she wanted antiretrovirals, so the physician prescribed them, then wrote into her medical record "hospice care," which was clearly a prognosis of having little time left. However, after a few months the woman came back and at that point, another physician asked her why "hospice care" was put into her medical record. The original physician responded, "Well clearly she was dying of AIDS." But then she saw the woman without her wheelchair, proudly showing off a sexy red dress she was wearing. She was healthy and very much alive!

During my tour with the Medical Director, I asked her who paid her salary and she said NIH. I felt so proud of her and our country when she told me what the U.S. was doing to help people with HIV/AIDS in South Africa, 8,000 miles from Washington, D.C.

I had arranged to stay with Christie Lane-Barlow, an epidemiologist pharmaceutical friend, whose husband was the head Park Ranger at the famed Kruger National park. They had a home and a small guest house inside Kruger Park where I stayed. We had lunch together while sitting on a log, watching animals come to drink in the stream below. We saw elephants roaming around and giraffes who walked gracefully, but indifferently, toward us only a short distance away. It was the best vacation I ever had. What a great feeling.

In 1993 I was living in Massachusetts and still getting involved whenever an issue arose that concerned HIV/AIDS. When legislation was introduced in that state that would allow an exchange of dirty needles to help curb the spread of HIV/AIDS, I took an interest. I scheduled a meeting with the Commonwealth of Massachusetts Senate President but was dismayed at his lack of interest in supporting that bill, plus his apparent uninformed position on the purpose and benefits of disposing of dirty needles. I told him I would find answers for him to educate his position. Then I had conversations with pharmacy friends and professionals at several hospitals who filled me in on the facts.

A short time later, I saw the Senate President at a reception and brought a one-page explanation on how to safely dispose of dirty needles. I said, "You promised you would sign the bill if I gave you the answers for the safe disposition of dirty needles. Well, sir – here it is." I watched him put it in his pocket, and felt that was the end of it, but very soon I learned he read it and then signed the legislation. People were dying from the spread of HIV through needle sharing, but the social stigma and perception of 'that unpleasantness' have a deterring effect that takes persistence and education to overcome. Once that legislation passed, I worked to help other states pass the same kind of legislation.

Today, after all the efforts, setbacks and successes, we need to educate young people about the dangers of using drugs, sharing needles, and having unprotected sex.

As of this writing the Federal and state CARE budgets total several billions of dollars. I like to think about the hundreds of thousands, maybe millions of people who then, and even now, are filling their HIV prescription needs through benefits made possible by ADAP.

World AIDS Day 2021's theme is global solidarity, shared responsibility. Each year on December 1, the world unites to show support for the estimated 40 million worldwide who have died of AIDS since 1981 and to remember those who have died from AIDS-related illnesses. Since it was first observed in 1988, HIV therapeutic medications are available to help people with HIV live long, healthy lives and prevent HIV transmissions. Pre-exposure prophylaxis (PrEP) and post-exposure prophylaxis (PEP) are readily available by prescription.

So many people are alive today who would surely have died, were it not for the ADAP initiatives. The bold action taken by so many unsung heroes who for so many years worked tirelessly and were committed to making a difference, is the legacy today and in all the tomorrows to come.

Note: At the end of 2019, 25.4M of the 38M people living with HIV were receiving antiretroviral therapies. COVID-19 has killed more than 4.5M of our fellow humans to date. AIDS has taken 36.3M humans to date. We still need to educate our young people about the dangers of unprotected sex and sharing needles in 2021 as much as we did 36 years ago.

ADDITIONAL RESOURCES

Africabridge.org Empowers Tanzanian families to protect, support and care for vulnerable children by helping villages implement sustainable social service and economic solutions. The impact on children and AIDS.

AIDS Healthcare Foundation is the global leader in HIV/AIDS treatment and care serves 1,355,493 people in 45 countries through global clinics offering HIV testing, antiretroviral and other HIV/AIDS prevention, and treatment services. Aidshealth.org

AIDS Action aac.org mission to stop the epidemic and related health inequities by elimination new infections. CDC.gov/hiv/basics/prep.html 800 232-4636

AIDS Alliance for Children, Youth & Families.

AIDS Service Organizations

American Pharmaceutical Research & Manufactures Association – HIV and COVID-19 Drugs

The aidsinstitute.org promotes action for social change through public policy research, advocacy and education

AIDS Coalition to Unleash Power (ACT-UP)

CDC.gov. Division of HIV/AIDS Prevention. 1 in 7 with HIV /161,000 in US don't know they are infected.

Community Access National Network (CANN.org) promotes and improves access to healthcare services and support for people living with HIV/AIDS and/or viral hepatitis through advocacy, education and networking.

Community for Creative Non-Violence (theccnv.org) mission to ensure that the rights of the homeless and poor are not infringed upon, and that every person has access to life's basic essentials – food, shelter, clothing and medical care. 1,350-bed Federal City Shelter is the largest and most comprehensive facility of its kind in America. Served over 5M meals to their residents since 1984. Restaurants, wholesale food distributors, and franchises donate over 150 tons of food to the shelter each year. Located at 425 Mitch Snyder Place (2nd St) NW Washington DC 20001 202 393-1909.

Health Resources and Services Administration/HHS

HIV/COVID-19 Operation Warp Speed

HIV/AIDS home test at local pharmacies

Manufacturers Abbott; Bristol Myers; GlaxoSmithKline-Pfizer ViiV; Gilead Sciences; Johnson & Johnson; Merck; Pfizer

National Coalition of STD Directors (NCSDDC.org) represents health department STD directors, their support staff, and community-based partners throughout the nation.

National Institutes of Health Office of AIDS Research FY 2021-2025 NIH Strategic Plan for HIV and HIV-Related research NIA.

National AIDS Treatment Advocacy Project (NATAP.org) up to the minute HIV treatment information, covering the latest in drug development and research. Educates about HIV and Hepatitis treatments.

National Association of State and Territorial AIDS Directors (NASTAD.org) represents HIV and hepatitis staff at state and territorial health departments.

Prevention Access Campaign (preventionaccess.org) Equal Access to the Prevention Revolution U=U. Undetectable =Untransmittable

Pre-Exposure Prophylaxis (PrEP) for those who are at very high risk of getting HIV to prevent infection by taking a pill every day. Brand name (Truvada) contains two medicines (tenofovir and emtricitabine). Reduces the risk by 99% when taken daily. It only protects against HIV, condoms are an important protection against other STDs.

Sheridangroupdc.com

THE NUTS & BOLTS OF GOVERNMENT:

HOW TO EFFECT CHANGE AT THE LOCAL, STATE AND NATIONAL LEVEL

The punishment of wise men
who refuse to take part
in the affairs of government
is to live under the
government of unwise men.

Plato

Content Overview

This booklet is not intended to be a Government 101 course. It is, however, a practical guide for those interested and willing to get involved in the political process on the local, state or national level.

Many issues are being decided daily by public policy makers, but much of this is done without consumer input and the voice of everyday people is important. This guidebook helps you to prepare for getting involved to make a difference. It's a practical outline on how Congress and Federal agencies operate and interact. What follows are read-it-now, use-it-now suggestions to help you navigate the system and understand how laws are made.

The beauty of politics is that you can begin at many different levels, and you don't need a particular degree or background to get involved. Most people care about and are directly affected by at least one issue — but you need to know what to do, and then how to make a difference.

There are many reasons people are motivated to get involved. You may want to meet new people who are interested in similar issues, or you may want to be a part of a community effort for an issue that affects people in your town, or you may want to help someone who is running for office.

This booklet will explain the relationship between getting a law passed, and then putting it into place through our regulatory process. Keep in mind that your voice is important. Lawmakers realize it is essential to get input from their constituents when they are looking at new legislation. Any letter you may write to your state legislator, Member of Congress, or to the President often gets referred to the appropriate state or Federal agency for response. It's the collective efforts of these letters that can prompt agencies to change a policy or clarify a position.

While you might feel your one letter is a drop in the bucket, make no mistake, your concern will be addressed, although it may take a few months to get an answer. You can effect change if you go about it in the right way — complaining does not do it. Try to get involved at the beginning of proposed legislation or regulations since waiting to voice your concern after the fact has far less clout.

Active participation can take many forms, ranging from writing a letter to a Representative, to running for office. Getting involved can take many forms but you have to take the first step.

A Step-by Step Approach

First, get to know your local and State Representatives and make an appointment to meet them and get acquainted before there is a crisis on an issue of concern. A 15-minute introductory visit will go a long way when you need to call upon your representative about a problem in the future.

It might seem scary to take that step but don't forget, those representatives don't get elected without your vote — your support makes a difference. These representatives might be in a small town municipal office, the State Capitol, or the Nation's Capitol. Regardless of their location, you are the reason they go to work every day!

First, it is important to know Who is in charge of What. There are always key decision makers whose vote or actions may change the course of events that affect you, your family, your town or state. If you don't like the way something is affecting you, or you want to suggest a better way of doing something, you must first identify the decision makers handling those issues.

What to Do

1. If it's a local level decision:
    ✓ collect information on how others like you are affected
    ✓ gather data to support your views
    ✓ know the arguments, both pro and con
    ✓ form a group of like-minded folks who have the same concerns as yours
    ✓ plan to visit the appropriate elected or appointed official or board who is/are in charge.

2. You can either visit in person, or write to those officials, but in either case when you do, you must be prepared by concisely stating the facts, having data, photos, or personal testimonials of support. Then present these by:

    1. writing a summary of the current situation and why it affects you and others
    2. explain in detail how it has affected you individually, and the community at large
    3. make suggested alternatives outlining the benefits of changes
    4. show short term and long term effects that improve your life and your community

3. If the board/agency is appointed and is not responsive, you can inform the appointing official that your concerns are not being acted upon.

However, if the board is elected and it is unresponsive you can work to defeat those individuals in the next election.

Becoming Part of the Legislative Process

Legislators need and want to know the views, attitudes, and opinions of their constituents. Although an elected official has many sources of information, the most effective communication he or she receives is from individual constituents. Without this information, legislators cannot be responsive to or representative of the people who elect them.

Communicating Your Views

All State and Federal representatives have district offices and most visit them at regular intervals. You can arrange to meet with these representatives. Here's how:

Contact that person's local office and make an appointment through the appointment/scheduling person. Give the purpose of the meeting, how many will attend and be sure to state if you want to discuss pending legislation or a specific issue. You can expect to be granted 5-10 minutes for Senator and 15-20 for a Member of Congress.

The state and local representatives may allow you an audience of up to half an hour. Be flexible in your availability as you may have to wait several weeks for an appointment, or you may be required to conduct your appointment through virtual means such as Zoom, Skype or Facetime.

Remember, as soon as the meeting commences the clock is ticking so have your "script" of your points to make, present those clearly, and stick to your agenda. Be sure to thank the person for the opportunity at the end. It is a good idea to rehearse your delivery a few times so you hear your speech out loud and can make the most of your time allowed.

Afterwards, follow up your visit with a letter, or email thanking your representative for meeting with you and a recap with a summary of the key points of your discussion, and answering any remaining questions, or further information they may have requested.

Always read over your message/letter at least twice to check for spelling, clarity and appropriateness.

Below is the correct format in addressing your representative when you write to them.

U.S. Senator
The Honorable (full name)
United States Senate
Washington, DC 20510

Dear Senator (surname)

U.S. Representative
The Honorable (full name)
U.S.House of Representatives
Washington, DC 20514

Dear Congressman/woman (surname)

State Senator
The Honorable (full name)
State Senate
State Capitol
City, State Zip

Dear Senator (surname):

State Representative
The Honorable (full name)
State House of Representatives
State Capitol
City, State Zip

Dear Mr./Mrs./Ms./ (surname):

In the content of your letter first identify yourself, and the purpose of your letter. If the content is focused on legislation, provide the bill number and title, if possible. Be brief, stick to the point and try to limit to one page. Offer constructive comments and alternatives to current legislation or issues of concern. Don't send a form letter if you can write your own letter. Expressing your views by phone are another means of reaching your representatives and these calls are treated like a letter, and many times are just as effective.

Give your name and telephone number at the outset of the call to register your opinion. If you express your view online you must live in their district in order for your views to be recognized as relevant.

Giving Personal Testimony at a Public Hearing

One effective means to convey your views is to address a group of decision makers. This is called a public hearing and you can find out when your representatives will conduct a public hearing, and the requirements for attending.

A hearing notice is available from the committee that will conduct the hearing. This notice will be a public announcement of why it is being held, what questions they are considering, and if any of those are important to you.

If you attend one of their hearings ahead of time this will familiarize you with the process of what happens. The hearing notice will generally indicate the length of time each witness will be allowed to speak, how many copies of testimony should be provided, or if oral testimony is by invitation only.

It is important that you know who you are representing if you decide to pursue this route. You must have the views of your group, or your own personal views clearly summarized to be aligned with the questions the panel is interested in hearing about.

When you review the prospective witness list who may be attending, keep in mind there will be others who may present opposing views. It is important to be able to adjust your own testimony and focus your points so that they challenge, rebut or disprove this opposing information. The panel or individuals conducting the testimony are interested in substantive research but also in personal and relevant experience that underscore your testimony's validity. Representatives must create policies that address the views of real people with real lives, not spreadsheets of dry facts and figures. Personal experiences are very compelling.

You will have a very short time to present your testimony, so it is more important to be relaxed, honest, and sincere in your delivery than grandstanding with a lot of unnecessary eloquence. Be prepared to give a two-minute executive summary as your time allotted may be cut at the last minute. Practice breathing and relaxation exercises to have a calm voice. Move your diaphragm OUT on inhalation. Move your diaphragm IN on exhalation. Alternate tightening your muscles and relaxing them. If you don't have a lot of time, yawn. It will calm you down. Avoid reading a prepared statement. It puts everyone to sleep.

Finally, expect chaos — there will be delays, equipment checks, cameras, interruptions for floor votes, and so on. Legislators will be conferring with staff while you speak but don't wait for them to look up and pay attention. Keep on speaking, do what you came to do and don't let the situation dissuade you from 'performing your best effort.'

Afterwards send copies of your written statement with a brief note to any of your own legislators who were not at the hearing and also a note of thanks and recognition to staff members who assisted you.

Legislative Process & How a Bill Becomes Law

THE CONGRESS

The U.S. Congress is composed of the Senate and the House of Representatives. The Senate has 100 members, two from each state, holding terms of office of six years. Every two years one-third of the Senate faces election. Both the Senate and the House hold sessions in the U.S. Capitol Building, but in different locations. The Senate Chamber is the North Wing of the building and the House convenes in the South Wing. The center of the capitol is the famous Rotunda and the capitol dome, a space which serves no legislative purpose and is for ceremonial events.

The House of Representatives has 435 members for the 50 states, who are elected every two years. The number of representatives in each state is determined by the total population of that state. That's why it is so important for every citizen to fill out the census forms. There are non-voting seats for Puerto Rico, the District of Columbia, Guam, the Virgin Islands, and American Samoa.

How it Begins – Introducing the Bill

A Congress – the actual time spent in legislative efforts-lasts for two years and is divided into two sessions. Congress meets in January after the

November elections to swear in new Members and/or every 4 years, the President. In each of these sessions they make laws, advises and consents on personnel appointments; advises and consents on treaties; and appropriate funds and then another group authorizes the amount of money to be spent and hold hearings.

Making laws starts with the introduction of one of four different proposals: the bill, the joint resolutions, the concurrent resolution or a simple resolution. A bill and joint resolution may begin its life first in either the House or the Senate.

Any member may introduce a bill whenever Congress is actually in session. All House bills are numbered H.R.____; Senate bills are numbered S._____. If the bill generates revenue, they must originate in the House. Then the bill is referred to an appropriate committee for consideration and approval.

The greatest amount of work is done in the assigned committee. During this stage public participation is solicited, and most easily influenced by special interest groups.

Next, Going to Committees

There are several types of committees who will review the bills that come to them for consideration.

1. Standing - Essentially a permanent committee having specific areas of jurisdiction. This committee is open to the public

2. Select/Special - This committee will investigate specific problems

3. Joint- This committee is comprised of members from both parties when separate committees would not be efficient.

4. Conference - They work out differences between versions of the same bill. Revisions are submitted to both Houses for consideration

5. Party - Each political party has a committee to make decisions on internal party matters, also called caucuses.

There will be at least one committee in each House that works on a particular issue. Sometimes a committee may need to also involve an appropriations committee (the money people) who would evaluate the costs involved and compare these to other spending priorities.

Seniority is powerful since those men/women usually will get to head a committee they are most interested in, either a policy issue or may be the appropriations committee.

Once a committee decides to send a bill to the full Congress, they prepare a committee report. It should include an explanation of what the bill is intended to accomplish. If it would change an existing law, that must be included, especially is it will repeal or change that law.

Then, the Floor Action

Now that a bill is written out and has been given the green light of the assigned committee, the next step is discussing it out in the open, this is called Floor Action. But before this can happen in the House, all bills are sent to the Rules Committee, which determines the amount of debate the bill will be allowed and, if floor amendments will be permitted. Following review, a bill is then placed on one of several calendars with a date for that floor debate. For the Senate however, there is no rules committee, and it can proceed to a debate.

In both the Senate and House the bill is debated on the floor and is generally open for amendment. Members prepare an amendment and run it by the Speaker or other chair of the particular committee before proposing it.

After all amendments have been considered, a vote is taken for final passage. This may take days or months before an amendment will be considered or dropped after quiet negotiations.

One chamber passes a bill and sends that to the other chamber for consideration. If the bill is reported out of committee favorably, it is returned to the House or Senate to receive a general order status in the Senate and Second Reading in the House, followed by a Third Reading where the bill is again subject to debate and amendment. Following either passage or defeat of a bill, a legislator may have the bill reconsidered. A motion to reconsider usually must be made within a specified time period. If defeated in one House, a bill is usually dead for the session.

If both chambers pass identical bills, the bill is transmitted to the President for executive action. If it has substantial amendments, it becomes necessary to go to conference.

A Detour to Approval: the Conference

The chamber that has the bill when it passes for the second time may request a conference with the other chamber to reconcile differences. Discussion is restricted to the differences. Then an agreement could be reached; or the bill could die in conference as a stalemate; or they may reach an agreement but if one of the Houses reject it, then the bill is considered dead.

If there is an authorization and an appropriation to implement a new law, the funding comes out of the Federal Treasury and is assigned to the agency that must implement the new or revised law.

Now, we should look at how the government spends money and how it decides where money goes. The U.S. government operates on a budget calendar that runs from October 1 through September 30. Each year, Congress must appropriate a specific amount of money to each department, agency, and program to provide funding for operations, personnel, equipment, and activities. Traditionally, the U.S. House of Representatives and the U.S. Senate agree together on a budget resolution in the spring that is then used to determine spending limits for twelve regular appropriations bills. The twelve appropriations bills then appropriate the funding for the federal government to use for the next budgetary year. The appropriation bills must be signed into the law by the President, although the budget resolution itself is not subject to his or her approval.

If Congress fails to appropriate the necessary funds for the federal government, the government shuts down as a result of the Antideficiency Act. The law "forbids federal officials from entering into financial obligations for which they do not have funding," such as buying ink, paying for electricity, or paying employees. Congress can avoid a government shutdown by passing a Continuing Resolution instead.

Standoffs between the President and Congress or between political parties, elections, and legislative matters complicate the budget process, frequently making the Continuing Resolution, a common occurrence. This allows the government to take its time making difficult financial decisions.

Federal agencies are disrupted during periods of reduced funding. With non-essential operations suspended, many agencies are forced to interrupt research projects, training programs, or other important functions. Its impact on day-to-day management can be severe, costing some employees the equivalent of several months time and paychecks.

Presidential Action

The President can sign the bill; veto the bill within 10 days of receiving it. Two-thirds of the Members in the originating house may vote to override the veto; take no action and thus the bill becomes law without the President's signature if not returned with objection within 10 days. If Congress had adjourned at the end of the second session and the President takes no action the bill dies and is called a 'pocket veto.'

Publication

To enact a valid law, it must be sent to the Administrator of General Services for publication. The bill is assigned a public law number and paginated for the Statutes-at-Large volume covering that session of the Congress. The numbers run chronologically starting anew at the beginning of each Congress, for example, the first public law of the 110th Congress is designated Public Law 110-1.

Statutes At Large

Provides a permanent collection of the laws of each session, the bound volumes - the United States Statutes at Large - are prepared by the General Services Administration.

United States Code

Contains a consolidation and codification of the general and permanent laws of the US arranged according to subject matter under 50 title headings.

Administrative Agencies — Regulations

Agencies such as the US Department of Health & Human Services (HHS) have been established within the Executive Branch to administer and implement our nation's laws.

Regulatory commissions are independent agencies established by Congress to regulate some aspect of the Nation's economy. These rules have the power of federal law.

An Overview

Before a bill is sought by the Administration, it usually is sent to the administrative agency responsible for its implementation. This informal process can assess the bill and suggest any changes. After the bill is introduced into Congress, it is again sent to the administrative agency when any revisions are proposed to clarify the bill.

When the bill is passed and becomes law, the agencies serve to translate the law into 'rules.' These rules are written as draft regulations to allow those who are affected by them to clearly understand their intent and legal requirements.

Administrative Procedure Act

The APA's requirement apply to both rule making and adjudications. Also referred to as agency 'Law Making' is the process for formulating, repealing, and amending a rule.

Federal Register System

Is made up of two publications – the Code of Federal Regulations (CFR) and the Federal Register. They contain an up-to-date listing of all existing federal rules and lists all permanent agency rules and is revised annually. The Federal register is a daily publication of federal agency action. It contains three types of documents: proposed rules, final rules, and notices.

Initially, with few exceptions, a rule must be presented to the public in the form of a 'proposed rule.' Agencies can issue a 'Notice of Inquiry or Advance Notice of Proposed Lawmaking' before constructing a proposed rule. The APA requires a 30 - 60 day comment period, when the public can submit written views and suggestions on the proposed rule. Comments received are published in the Comment Section of the Federal Register.

Once a proposed rule has satisfied the APA's requirements, the Agency can adopt the rule and issue a "Final Rule." The APA requires 30 days notice in the Federal Register that the rule has been adopted before it can become effective. Finally, if the agency does not comply with the APA, it can be sued.

Lobbying

Each state has different lobbying requirements. Check with the Secretary of State for forms and any costs. Generally, if you're trying to influence legislation AND are being paid to do so, you should register or suffer the state's penalty.

There is no real mystique about becoming a registered lobbyist. It is considered lobbying at the Federal level when one is paid for attempting to influence the passage or defeat of legislation by the Congress. Before doing any lobbying one must register with the Clerk of the House of Representatives and the Secretary of the Senate. This may have changed since writing this booklet. But registration is required each quarter with a detailed report of all money received and expended, to whom, for what purposes, the names of any papers, periodicals, magazines editorials used to support or oppose legislation.

Most importantly, effective lobbyist should always be honest. Don't just present your or your group's views, you should present the opposing views of any legislation you are trying to influence.

How to Run for Local Public Office

If you are interested in public service, you might start by getting appointed to a local board or committee. Or run for local public office. Here are some helpful hints.

Getting Organized

Decide on an issue(s) to campaign on. If you are passionate about any issue, climate change, health care, any subject where you want to make a difference, there probably is a group that can use your help and support. You could start with volunteering with a group you admire or giving them some financial support. Let them know of your interest and find out how best you can help. You will get to know the people and the issues and will give you the background to decide if you want to pursue running for office.

Set up an election campaign committee with friends and colleagues who would support your candidacy. Have them ask local groups, both political and non-political, for lists of members. Try to acquire lists of potential contributors and appoint a finance person. Choose a seasoned campaign manager who may need to be paid. Next, fill out nomination papers. Your local town or city hall clerk can give you the information you'll need — how many signatures are required to be on the ballot, when they're due, etc. Take several copies of the nomination papers with you so you can have all your committee members gather signatures. Copy these signatures before filing. Send thank you notes to the names on the list. Have someone find their phone numbers and contact info for follow up.

Put an announcement of your candidacy with your picture in all the local newspapers. List all your qualifications, education, positions held, which political party you belong to etc.

Make out volunteer recruitment cards indicating the help you will need:

      ___will help distribute literature
      ___will hold a coffee hour
      ___will work at the polls
      ___will contribute $_____
      ___will put signs up (if allowed)
      ___will make telephone calls
      ___will help with mailing

Get the voter lists from your election officials so you can see who usually votes, their party affiliation or if they have no party affiliation. This is all public information. It will have their name, age, address and when and how they voted.

You could mail a flyer to people who are not registered to vote informing them of registration dates and how they can do it online if your state allows. Remind them of the date for election and where they can vote, either by mail or in person.

Canvass votes in person or other contact by phone, email. Ask every person you know for their vote — do not take anyone for granted.

Keep a list of
1. A positive candidate vote
2. Leaning toward
3. Undecided
4. Against the candidate.

Publicity

Try to keep your name before the voters as often as you can since name recognition is a big factor in an election.

Always wear a pin or tag to identify yourself as a candidate when you're shopping, going to church, etc.

Have political cards printed with your picture. Postcard size so they can be mailed at the lower rate.

Elect (later Re-Elect _____ for _____
Qualifications_____
Why vote for me_____
When to vote_____

Have some area left blank on the back for thank you notes with your picture and qualifications on one side only. Have the rest printed with a message on the back for supporters to send out.

Dear_____,

_____is a friend of mine and is a candidate for

_____. I feel he/she is qualified for the position.
I hope you will consider him/her when you vote on (DATE)_____.

Thanks,

Signature_____

Ask all your friends and acquaintances to complete at least ten postcards. Either have them mail them or you can collect them and mail them to make sure they have written them out. Keep a list of who they were mailed to. Mail them a couple of weeks before the election. Try to get supporters to contribute the stamps. Be sure to get your campaign material printed by a union printer if your state or printer union requires the 'union bug.' Especially, if you want to receive support from unions.

Solicit names of people, prominent and otherwise, who will sign an ad endorsing your candidacy (with picture). Have them sign an appropriate newspaper release form. Accept their donation and record it, as well as all cashed checks.

Set up coffee hours or receptions in peoples' homes or public locations. Bring someone with you who will make sure the host or hostess will quiet the group so you can speak. Friends can pass out campaign postcards and keep track of who got them and how many each received. Determine who will mail the postcards.

Put an article in the paper for each event along with the name of the person hosting it. Distribute leaflets at hockey games, the corner store, the dump, wherever people congregate. Do not put literature in mailboxes, it's illegal. When distributing by hand, write 'Sorry you were not home' or similar and sign it. If it has a note people will read it.

Don't neglect senior citizens. IF you know any contacts in assisted living or senior housing, offer to have a coffee hour in their recreation room. Establish a senior citizens advisory committee as well as a 'kitchen cabinet' of people whom you will meet with every week to go over strategy and outreach. They will be our eyes and ears in the community and give you advise on what you might want to consider.

The Day of the Election

Decide if you will make phone calls on election day. Have callers remind constituents to vote and offer a ride to the polls. You can stand at the polls and introduce yourself but do NOT try to pass out any literature or shake hands unless the voters appear to want to. Have your friends stand with you.

Other Tips

✓ Smile a lot and give a FIRM handshake

✓ Don't mention opponents name — refer to as 'opponent' or 'incumbent.'

✓ Be bold — campaign in the rain, in the snow and or under other unpleasant conditions. You may win some sympathy votes.

✓ Send thank you notes to every person that does anything for you.

ACKNOWLEDGMENTS

In any undertaking that is of so personal an adventure such as this one, there is inevitably a rollercoaster of stress, elation, anxiety and not a few tears. One guiding force that kept the course and helped focus the effort was author Barbara Hesselgrave who found, interviewed and wrote the recollections of many of the State AIDS Directors who graciously gave permission to use their stories. She was essential in converting my policy-wonk descriptions to prose and put in more hours far beyond the call of duty to ensure I would be happy with the final manuscript. This book would not have been written without her writing, good humor and patience. Sue Brite helped with proof reading and gave me confidence that it would get published. Thanks to Jim Garrison who formatted this book for publication.

I am grateful and extremely thankful and blessed for all their help and for the support of my children: Kathy Ryan, Karen Sullivan, Patti Keville, Tom Keville, and Bill Keville.

Many others played a crucial role in both the development and completion of this project and I owe many thanks to them for their willingness, endurance and patience to fulfill the goals of this important memoir. For some of them it was a visit to the past, for others it was a gift to the future, but they are to a one all important.

My thanks then, go to you Jeanne Blake, Jay Adams, Bill Arnold, Jim Arvantes, Barry Childs, Lanny Cross, Denise Steinbach, Jim Driscoll, Teri Eyster, Gregg Gonsalves, David Harvey, Dwayne Haught, Kathie Hiers, Jules Levin, Michael Montgomery, Philip Orlander, Murray Penner, David Poole, Chris Rivera, Julie Scofield, Pamela Smart, William Schuyler, Tom Sheridan, Liza Solomon, Rich Tafel, Dr. Paul Volberding, Dr. Thad Zajdowicz, Christie Lane-Barlow, David Secor, Richard Schulman.

A portion of the proceeds will be contributed to the non-profit **www.africabridge.org**.

ABOUT THE AUTHOR

Dorothy Keville founded the AIDS Drug Assistance Program Working Group and managed the Federal Interagency Task Force on Homelessness comprised of 13 Federal agencies. Additionally, she co-founded Africa Bridge, a global organization dedicated to the care of children whose parents died of HIV/AIDS. Earlier in her career, she was Director of the Office of Litigation at the MA Department of Mental Health.

An accomplished SAG/AFTRA actor, Dorothy held the lead role in the independent film *Fish & Chips*, which chronicles life with Alzheimer's disease. She earned her M.Ed. in Human Social Services Administration at Antioch University, Harvard campus. Dorothy's volunteer activities include work with Daystar food pantry and chairing the Columbarium Committee at Glastonbury Abbey in Hingham, MA.

She is the proud mother of five children, 12 grandchildren and three great grandchildren. Today she resides in St. Petersburg, FL. Dorothy welcomes your communication at **dorothykeville@icloud.com**.

CPSIA information can be obtained
at www.ICGtesting.com
Printed in the USA
FSHW021639031121
85849FS

9 780578 302584